FUTURE
English for Results

2

TESTS and TEST PREP
with **Exam***View*® *Assessment Suite*

Jennifer Gaudet

Daniel S. Pittaway

Series Consultants

Beatriz B. Díaz

Ronna Magy

Federico Salas-Isnardi

PEARSON

Longman

Future 2 Tests and Test Prep

Staff credits: The people who made up the *Future 2 Tests and Test Prep* team, representing editorial, production, design, and manufacturing, are: Rhea Banker, Aerin Csigay, Mindy De Palma, Nancy Flaggman, Irene Frankel, Katherine Keyes, Linda Moser, Barbara Sabella, and Julie Schmidt
Cover design: Rhea Banker
Cover photo: Kathy Lamm/Getty Images
Text composition: TSI Graphics
Text font: Minion Regular
Text design: Barbara Sabella

Photo Credits: All original photography by David Mager. Page 1(L) Shutterstock, (M) Shutterstock, (R) Shutterstock; 8 Ned Frisk Photography/Corbis; 10(TL) Don Hammond/ agefotostock, (TR) Dae Seung Seo/Getty Images, (BL) Shutterstock, (BM) Shutterstock.com, (BR) Shutterstock; 18 Shutterstock; 24(1) Frederic Cirou/Jupiterimages, (2) Shutterstock, (3) Adam Hunter/Tiger Advertising /www.tigeradvertising.ca, (4) Adam Hunter/Tiger Advertising / www.tigeradvertising.ca; 25(1) Shutterstock, (2) Shutterstock, (3) Shutterstock, (4) Adam Hunter/ Tiger Advertising /www.tigeradvertising.ca; 29(L) Lawrence Sawyer/iStockphoto.com, (M) Nicole S. Young/iStockphoto.com, (R) SpencerGrant/PhotoEdit; 33(1) Shutterstock, (2) BananaStock/ SuperStock, (3) Comstock/Jupiterimages, (4) Shutterstock; 34(1) Jupiterimages/BananaStock/ Alamy, (2) Robert Warren/Getty Images, (3) Purestock/Getty Images, (4) Tony Freeman/ PhotoEdit; 37 Purestock/Getty Images; 52(1) Image Source/Getty Images, (2) Stephen Simpson/ Getty Images, (3) Daniel Templeton/Alamy, (4) Blend Images/SuperStock; 56 Hurewitz Creative/ Corbis; 71(L) Andersen Ross/Brand X/Corbis, (R) GOGO Images/SuperStock; 74 M Stock/Alamy; 75(L) Blend Images/Alamy, (M) Fotolia.com, (R) Photo Alto/Alamy; 80(1) Blend Images/Alamy, (2) Royalty-Free Division/Masterfile, (3) Jeff Greenberg/Alamy, (4) Rhoda Sidney/The Image Works; 81(L) Fotolia.com, (R) Hallgerd/Fotolia; 84 Shutterstock; 103(TL) Randy Faris/Corbis, (TM) Taylor Jorjorian/Alamy, (TR) Burke/Triolo Productions/Brand X/Corbis, (BL) iStockphoto. com, (BM) iStockphoto.com, (BR) Rene Mansi/iStockphoto.com; 107(1) Blend Images/ SuperStock, (2) Cindy Charles/PhotoEdit, (3) David M. Grossman/The Image Works, (4) David Bacon/The Image Works.

ISBN-13: 0-13-240880-5
ISBN-10: 9780132408806

Printed in the United States of America
5 6 7 8 9 10 —V0UD— 20 19 18 17 16

Contents

Welcome to *Future 2 Tests and Test Prep.* This package (containing a book, audio CD, and e-CD) provides all the assessment tools you need:

- The **Test Prep** section at the beginning of the book contains test-taking strategy worksheets and a sample unit test.
- The **Printed Unit Tests** in the book test students' mastery of the content presented in the Student Book units. The audio CD accompanies these tests.
- The **Exam*View*® *Assessment Suite*** on the e-CD offers a wealth of additional ways to assess students. Teachers can create their own unique tests or print or customize already prepared, multilevel unit tests in addition to midterm and final tests.

TEST PREP

Many adult ESL students are unfamiliar with standardized tests. The Test Prep section contains reproducible worksheets that will prepare students for both the printed unit tests in this book and for any standardized tests they may have to take, such as the CASAS Life and Work Series. You will find the following worksheets on pages viii-xvi:

- How to Use an Answer Sheet
- Instructions for the Sample Unit Test
- Sample Unit Test (Listening, Grammar, and Life Skills sections)
- Answer Key and Audio Script for the Sample Unit Test (the teacher may choose not to distribute this to students)
- Standardized Tests: Practice Questions
- Test-Taking Strategies

You can distribute the worksheets to your class over a period of time (for example, one or two pages a week). Alternatively, you can wait until students are close to the time they will be tested or post-tested and then go over all the material in one session.

To administer the Sample Unit Test:

- Go over the Instructions for the Sample Unit Test worksheet with your class.
- Make copies of the test and of the blank Answer Sheet on page 113. Distribute the copies to your students. Have them bubble in their test answers on the Answer Sheet.
- The audio for the sample listening questions can be found on the audio CD, Tracks 2–4. Play each track twice, pausing for 10 to 20 seconds between each play.
- Check answers using the Answer Key and the Audio Script for the Sample Unit Test on page xiv.

The Sample Unit Test (with the exception of the grammar section) is similar in format and content to the CASAS Life and Work Reading and Listening Series tests, but not identical to them. The CASAS website (www.casas.org) offers additional information, such as practice test questions, that you may find useful.

PRINTED UNIT TESTS

The are 12 printed Unit Tests in this test booklet. They are designed to assess how well students have mastered the material presented in each unit of the Student Book. Each test contains the following sections:

- Listening
- Grammar
- Vocabulary
- Life Skills
- Reading

The Listening, Vocabulary, Life Skills, and Reading sections of the tests emulate the look and feel of the CASAS Life and Work Reading and Listening Series tests. All the sections use a multiple-choice format, modeling the format students will encounter in standardized tests.

Listening

The Listening section includes a variety of item types and is divided into three parts: Listening I, Listening II, and Life Skills I. (Life Skills I does not appear in every test.)

In the **Listening I** and **Life Skills I** sections, students listen to test items and look at the answer choices on the test page. The answer choices are usually pictures.

In **Listening II,** both the questions and the answer choices are on the audio CD. There are two types of questions. In the first type, students hear a statement or question and have to choose the appropriate response to that statement or question. In the second type, the students hear a short conversation and have to answer a comprehension question about that conversation.

The directions and the answer choices appear on the Listening II test page. This is different from the CASAS test, where students are not given answer choices to look at for these item types. In other words, students bubble in their answers on the answer sheet, but they do not see the questions or answer choices in print. If your students need extra support, give them the second page of the test, the Listening II page, when you distribute the test. But if you wish to emulate CASAS more closely, you should omit the second page of the test.

Grammar

Students are asked to complete short conversations that contain examples of the grammar points presented in the unit.

Vocabulary

Students identify pictures of vocabulary items that were presented in the vocabulary lesson(s) of the unit.

Life Skills

The Life Skills section may include both listening and reading items. In the Life Skills Listening section (Life Skills I), students look at three different pictures and listen to a sentence or conversation, and then choose the correct picture. In the Life Skills Reading section (either Life Skills I or Life Skills II), students read a brief text or look at pictures. Then they answer questions about the text or pictures.

Reading

Students read a short paragraph that reflects the grammar and themes covered in the unit and then answer comprehension questions about it.

Answer Keys and Audio Scripts

You will find an Answer Key and an Audio Script for each printed Unit Test at the back of this book. The Answer Key is an answer sheet with the correct answers for the test bubbled in. It also provides diagnostic information about each test question.

Administering and Scoring Printed Unit Tests

To administer a printed Unit Test:

- Find the test you want in this book and photocopy it.
- Decide whether or not you want students to look at the Listening II page as they take the test (see the Listening II section). Either include or omit the Listening II page when you distribute the test.
- Make copies of the blank Answer Sheet on page 113 and distribute them to your students. Ask students to bubble in their test answers on the Answer Sheet.
- Start with the Listening Section of the test. Locate the appropriate audio track on the audio CD. We recommend that you play each track twice, pausing for 10 to 20 seconds between each play. This will approximate how listening is presented on standardized tests.
- Each 33-item test is designed to take 25 to 30 minutes to administer.

To score a printed Unit Test:

- Collect your students' bubbled-in Answer Sheets.
- Locate the Answer Key for the test at the back of this book. To create a scoring mask, photocopy the Answer Key and punch a hole in each bubbled-in answer.

When you lay this scoring mask over a student's Answer Sheet, you can easily see if the student has bubbled in the correct answer. If the bubble is not filled in, then simply mark an X on the unmarked bubble with a colored pencil.

- Count the number of correctly bubbled in answers on the student's Answer Sheet. Each correct answer is worth three points. To calculate a percentage score for your students, multiply the number of correct answers by three and add one point.

The Answer Key provides the objective that each item tests, along with the lesson and page number in the Student Book where the material was presented. If a student answers a particular item incorrectly, you will then know which competency the student has missed and/or in which lesson he or she may need further practice.

EXAM*VIEW*® *ASSESSMENT SUITE*

The **Exam***View*® *Assessment Suite* can be used either to supplement the printed Unit Tests or in place of them. With **Exam***View*, you can create or customize your own tests for students. Alternatively, you can choose to simply print out Unit, Midterm, or Final tests that have already been prepared for you and administer them to your class.

For detailed information on how to install the **Exam***View* software and use it to create, customize, and print out tests, please refer to the *TO THE TEACHER* PDF located on the *Future 2* **Exam***View Assessment Suite* e-CD. The installation instructions in the back of the book will tell you how to find this document.

Exam*View* Unit Tests

The prepared **Exam***View* Unit Tests are designed to address the needs of multilevel classes. Each Unit Test is offered at three different levels: **pre-level**, **on-level**, and **above-level**. You can choose to divide your class into three different groups and to administer a different version of a test to each group simultaneously. You can also use different versions of a test to diagnose a student's level.

The **Exam***View* unit tests have the same general structure as the printed unit tests in the book, with a series of multiple choice questions that test listening, grammar, vocabulary, life skills, and reading skills. However, the **Exam***View* unit tests do not follow the CASAS testing format as closely as the printed unit tests do. Another difference is that there are two separate types of tests for each unit. The first is a Listening Test, in PDF format, and the second is an **Exam***View* Test, containing grammar, vocabulary, life skills, and reading items.

The Listening Tests are offered in PDF format to make them easier for teachers to administer. There are separate pre-level, on-level, and above level PDFs for each listening test. All three levels share the same audio. They also share the same basic structure: students listen to longer conversations (similar to the listenings in the Student Book) and then answer comprehension questions about them.

Meanwhile, grammar, vocabulary, life skills, and reading skills are tested in the **Exam***View* unit tests. There are separate pre-level, on-level, and above-level **Exam***View* tests for each unit. Again, all three levels share the same basic structure.

Exam*View* Midterm and Final Tests

The **Exam***View* Midterm and Final Tests are offered at on-level only in order to provide an objective, standardized way to assess all your students at the halfway point and at the end of the course. The tests have a total of 66 items each. The Midterm tests the content presented in Units 1–6 and the Final covers Units 7–12. As with the Unit Tests, the Listening Midterm and Final Tests are in PDF format, and grammar, vocabulary, life skills, and reading items are in (on-level only) **Exam***View* question banks.

Administering and Scoring Exam*View* Tests

To administer an **Exam***View* Test:

- You can administer **Exam***View* Tests via computer or simply print them out and distribute them to your students.

- If you want to administer a multilevel Unit Test, divide your class into pre-level, on-level, and above-level groups.
- Locate the appropriate PDFs and **Exam**_View_ tests on the e-CD. For example, if you wanted to administer the pre-level tests for Unit 1, you would print out the pre-level Listening test PDF and the pre-level **Exam**_View_ test for Unit 1. (Please refer to the _TO THE TEACHER_ PDF for more information on how to select the PDFs or tests you need.)
- Distribute the tests to your students. (Note: the Answer Keys for the **Exam**_View_ tests print out automatically at the end of the test. Make sure you do not distribute the Answer Key to your students along with the test!)
- If you are printing out tests for your students, make copies of the blank answer sheet on page 113. Distribute two copies to each student. One copy is for the Listening Test, and the other copy is for the **Exam**_View_ Test.
- Start with the Listening Test. Play the appropriate audio tracks for the test. Have students fill in the correct number of bubbles on the first answer sheet (usually, for six test items). Then collect the listening answer sheets.
- Next, administer the **Exam**_View_ test for the unit. Have students bubble in the second answer sheet. Collect the answer sheets when students are finished.
- Allow 25-30 minutes for students to complete the Listening Test and the **Exam**_View_ test for each unit. Allow 50-60 minutes for a midterm or final.

To score an **Exam**_View_ Test:
- Collect your students' bubbled-in answer sheets.
- Locate the Answer Keys for the test. The Answer Keys and Audio Script for each Listening test are in PDF format in the same folder as the listening test. For the Unit Listening Tests, there is a pre-level Listening Answer Key, an on-level Listening Answer Key, and an above-level Listening Answer Key. Note that there is only one Audio Script for all three levels of the Unit Tests. The Answer Keys for the **Exam**_View_ tests will print out automatically at the end of each test, as noted above.
- Count the number of correctly bubbled in answers on each student's Answer Sheets. Add the scores of the Listening Test and the **Exam**_View_ test together. Then score the **Exam**_View_ Unit Tests as you would a printed Unit Test. For the 66-item Midterm or Final test, multiply the number of correct answers by 3, add 2 free points, and divide the result by 2 to get a percentage score.

You can find detailed diagnostic information about each test item in the answer keys, including the following:
- Level of difficulty (DIF): Pre-level, On-level, or Above-level
- Reference (REF): Student Book level and unit being tested
- Learning objective (OBJ): the learning objective of the item (as found in the _Scope & Sequence_/Student Book unit lesson)
- National standard (NAT): the CASAS competency being tested, if applicable
- Skill (SKL): the skill being tested (listening, grammar, vocabulary, life skills, or reading)

As with the printed Unit Test Answer Keys, you can use this diagnostic information to determine the competencies and/or lessons in which your students need more practice.

HOW TO USE AN ANSWER SHEET

For many tests, you use an Answer Sheet to mark, or bubble in, your answers. You must use a #2 pencil. You do not mark your answers on the test. A machine may score your answers. The machine reads and records the pencil marks on the Answer Sheet.

First, you need to fill in some personal information on the Answer Sheet.

Here is an example of the Answer Sheet in this book:

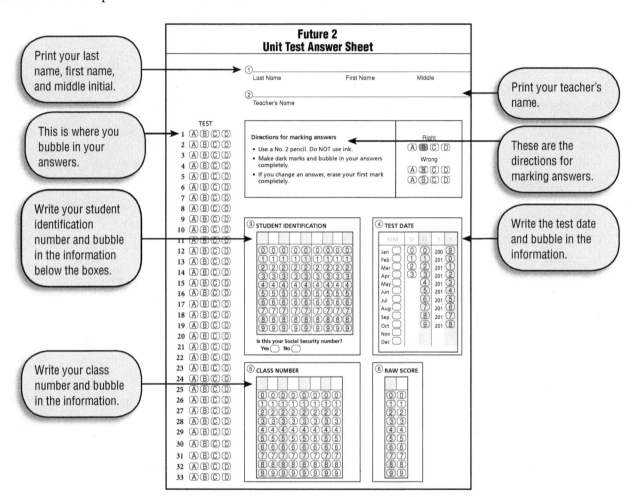

INSTRUCTIONS FOR THE SAMPLE UNIT TEST

This sample test is like the Unit Tests in this book. It has Listening, Grammar, and Life Skills section questions. Follow the directions carefully.

Listening Section

All the questions in the Listening section have three answer choices. You will hear each question two times. Here are examples of the three types of listening questions:

Example 1: You listen and choose the correct picture.
You will hear: *It's a desk.*

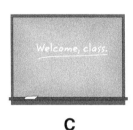

A   **B**   **C**

correct answer: **A**

Example 2: You listen and choose the correct response to the statement or question.
You will hear: *Can I borrow a pen?*

    A. It's a cell phone.
    B. Turn off the computer.
    C. Sure.

correct answer: **C**

Example 3: You listen to a conversation and choose the correct answer to a question about it.
You will hear: **F:** Who is he?
                   M: He's a student.

                    Who is the man?

                    A. He's a student.
                    B. He's a principal.
                    C. He's a teacher.

correct answer: **A**

Grammar and Life Skills sections

The questions in the Grammar section have three answer choices. You choose the correct answer to complete a conversation. The questions in the Life Skills section have four answer choices. You read or look at a picture and then answer a question about it.

SAMPLE UNIT TEST

 LISTENING I

(Track 2) Look at the pictures and listen. What is the correct answer: A, B, or C?

1.

A   **B**   **C**

2.

A   **B**   **C**

 **LISTENING II**

(Track 3) **Listen to the question and three answers. What is the correct answer: A, B, or C?**

3. A. It's a cell phone.
    B. Turn off the computer.
    C. Sure.

4. A. They're cell phones.
    B. Sure.
    C. Don't look at the book.

(Track 4) **Listen to the conversation. Then listen to the question and three answers. What is the correct answer: A, B, or C?**

5. A. the office
    B. the computer lab
    C. the dictionary

6. Who is the man?
    A. He's a student.
    B. He's the office assistant.
    C. He's the teacher.

GRAMMAR

Complete each conversation. What is the correct answer: A, B, or C?

7. **A:** Anita doesn't understand.

   B: OK. Please help _____.

   A. her
   B. us
   C. me

8. **A:** Is _____ your cell phone?

   B: Yes, it is.

   A. these
   B. that
   C. those

LIFE SKILLS

Read. What is the correct answer: A, B, C, or D?

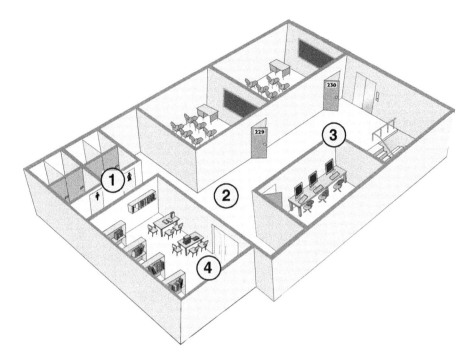

9. What is ①?

   A. It's a cafeteria.

   B. It's an elevator.

   C. It's a library.

   D. It's a restroom.

10. Where is the computer lab?

    A. It's next to the cafeteria.

    B. It's next to the restroom.

    C. It's across from the classroom.

    D. It's next to the office.

ANSWER KEY AND AUDIO SCRIPT FOR THE SAMPLE UNIT TEST

Answer Key

1. C	3. C	5. B	7. A	9. D
2. C	4. A	6. C	8. B	10. C

Audio Script

LISTENING I

(Track 2) Look at the pictures and listen. What is the correct answer: A, B, or C?

1. It's a book.

2. Take out your dictionary, please.

LISTENING II

(Track 3) Listen to the question and three answers. What is the correct answer: A, B, or C?

3. Can I borrow a piece of paper?

    A. It's a cell phone.

    B. Turn off the computer.

    C. Sure.

4. What are these called in English?

    A. They're cell phones.

    B. Sure.

    C. Don't look at the book.

(Track 4) Listen to the conversation. Then listen to the question and three answers. What is the correct answer: A, B, or C?

5. F: Is the computer lab open?

  M: Yes, it is.

    What is open?
    A. the office
    B. the computer lab
    C. the dictionary

6. F: Who is he?

  M: He's the teacher.

    Who is the man?
    A. He's a student.
    B. He's the office assistant.
    C. He's the teacher.

STANDARDIZED TESTS: PRACTICE QUESTIONS

Many standardized tests begin with a practice page. Here is an example of a practice page. Read through the questions below and make sure you understand how to answer them.

When you take a standardized test, find the practice page. It says *Practice.* Look for the practice answer box on the answer sheet. Use a pencil. Bubble in your answer. Ask the tester for help if you do not understand the directions. When the test begins, you are not allowed to talk. You cannot ask for or give help.

READING TEST

Practice 1

Here's a quarter.

A

B

C

D

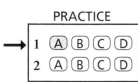
PRACTICE

→ 1 (A) (B) (C) (D)
  2 (A) (B) (C) (D)

Practice 2

SUN.	MON.	TUES.	WED.	THURS.	FRI.	SAT.
	computer class		English class			

When is the English class?

    A. It's on Monday.

    B. It's on Tuesday.

    C. It's on Wednesday.

    D. It's on Thursday.

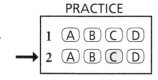
PRACTICE

  1 (A) (B) (C) (D)
→ 2 (A) (B) (C) (D)

TEST-TAKING STRATEGIES

Preparing to Take a Test
- Get a lot of sleep the night before the test.
- Eat a meal or snack before the test.
- Bring two sharpened #2 pencils.
- Bring a pencil eraser.
- Bring a ruler or a blank piece of paper.
- Arrive early to the testing room.
- Make sure you can easily see and hear the tester.
- Turn off your cell phone.
- Try to relax and do your best! Good luck!

Taking a Test
- As soon as you start a test section, look through the section to see how many questions there are.
- Don't spend too much time on any one question. If you don't know the answer, guess and then move on to the next item. You can circle the item number and come back to it at the end if you have time.
- For a listening section: Look at the answer choices for the question. Then listen to the directions and the question. Remember that for some questions, both questions and answer choices may be on the CD. You will hear the questions and the answer choices.
- For all other sections: Read the material. Read the question carefully. Read all the answer choices.
- Think: Which is the best answer? Look at the answer choices again. Eliminate answers you know are not correct.
- Choose the best answer.
- Make sure you mark your answer on the correct line on the answer sheet. Use a ruler to help you, or use a blank piece of paper to cover the lines below the line you are working on.
- Check each time that you bubble in the circle on the correct line for the question you are answering.
- Do not change the first answer you mark unless you are sure that it is wrong.
- Erase completely any answers you have changed. Fill in only ONE answer on each line. Erase all extra marks on your answer sheet.
- When you finish, if there is time, always recheck your answers.
- If you cannot answer many questions, it is OK. Raise your hand. Tell the tester. You may be excused from taking the rest of the test.

Unit 1 Test

LISTENING I

(Track 5) Look at the pictures and listen. What is the correct answer: A, B, or C?

1.

A	B	C

2.

A	B	C

💿 LISTENING II

(Track 6) Listen to the question and three answers. What is the correct answer: A, B, or C?

3. A. Where are you from?

   B. Oh, that's nice.

   C. It's a very beautiful country.

4. A. No, we're from Hawaii.

   B. Yes, we're in Mr. Carter's English class.

   C. Yes, it's a beautiful country.

(Track 7) Listen to the conversation. Then listen to the question and three answers. What is the correct answer: A, B, or C?

5. A. She is working.

   B. She is coming to the party.

   C. She is having a party.

6. A. He's talkative.

   B. He's tall and thin.

   C. He's quiet and attractive.

GRAMMAR

Complete each conversation. What is the correct answer: A, B, or C?

7. **A:** Ingrid has blue eyes.
   B: No. She _____ blue eyes. She has brown eyes.

   A. has
   B. doesn't have
   C. don't have

8. **A:** What is your brother like?
   B: He's tall _____ handsome.

   A. and
   B. is
   C. but

9. **A:** My friends are heavy.
   B: My friends _____.

   A. are, too
   B. aren't, either
   C. is, too

10. **A:** Does Josh have a lot of friends?
    B: No. He's outgoing _____ he doesn't have a lot of friends.

    A. but
    B. and
    C. also

11. **A:** Do you go to school?
    B: Yes. I'm a student and my sister _____.

    A. aren't, either
    B. is, too
    C. are, too

12. **A:** Is Jamal in your English class this year?
    B: No. He isn't in my class and Fatma _____.

    A. isn't, either
    B. is, too
    C. aren't, either

13. **A:** Is Carmen pretty?
    B: Yes, _____.

    A. she isn't
    B. he is
    C. she is

14. **A:** Where _____ they from?
    B: They're from Vietnam.

    A. is
    B. were
    C. are

15. **A:** What's Tamara like?
    B: Tamara is friendly and her husband _____.

    A. is, too
    B. am, too
    C. are, too

16. **A:** _____ you Eva's daughter?
    B: No, I'm not.

    A. Is
    B. Are
    C. Am

17. **A:** Are you shy?
    B: Yes, _____.

    A. I'm
    B. I'm not
    C. I am

18. **A:** Brent _____ handsome.
    B: I know. But he's really nice.

    A. has
    B. hasn't
    C. isn't

19. **A:** My friend is from Mexico _____ lives in Canada.
    B: Oh. Is she a student there?

    A. and she
    B. she
    C. but she

20. **A:** Ms. Castillo is nice.
    B: Well, she's sweet _____ she's a little moody.

    A. has
    B. but
    C. and

21. **A:** Carla _____ really long brown hair.
    B: Yes. It's straight, too.

    A. has
    B. have
    C. is

VOCABULARY

Read. What is the correct answer: A, B, C, or D?

Miguel

Jin

22. What does Miguel have?

A. a mustache

B. a goatee

C. a beard

D. long hair

23. What does Jin look like?

A. He has a beard.

B. He has curly hair.

C. He has black hair.

D. He is bald.

Read. What is the correct answer: A, B, C, or D?

Ellen

Selena

24. What does Ellen look like?

    A. She is tall and thin.

    B. She is heavy.

    C. She has long, black hair.

    D. She is short and has long, curly hair.

25. What does Selena look like?

    A. She is tall and thin.

    B. She is heavy.

    C. She is bald.

    D. She has long, straight hair.

LIFE SKILLS

Read. What is the correct answer: A, B, C, or D?

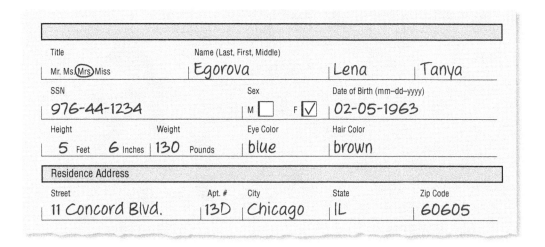

26. What is the applicant's last name?

    A. Lena

    B. Tanya

    C. Egorova

    D. Mrs.

27. How tall is the applicant?

    A. 1963

    B. 5 feet 6 inches

    C. 130 pounds

    D. 976-44-1234

28. What does the applicant look like?

    A. She is very short.

    B. She has black hair and brown eyes.

    C. She has blue eyes and brown hair.

    D. She is very heavy.

Read. What is the correct answer: A, B, C, or D?

29. What color are Teresa's eyes?

A. black

B. brown

C. blue

D. green

30. What is Teresa's date of birth?

A. 5-04

B. 09-30-1979

C. 05-15-2007

D. 09-30-2012

31. How much does she weigh?

A. 115

B. 68102

C. 5-04

D. 2012

READING

Read. What is the correct answer: A, B, C, or D?

Vinicio and Marisol are from Puerto Rico. They are brother and sister. They have brown hair and brown eyes. Vinicio's hair is short and wavy, but Marisol's hair is wavy and long. Marisol isn't shy, and Vinicio isn't either. Marisol is a teacher, and Vinicio is, too.

32. What are Marisol and Vinicio like?

  A. They are shy.

  B. They are tall and slim.

  C. They are students.

  D. They aren't shy.

33. What do Marisol and Vinicio do?

  A. They are from Puerto Rico.

  B. Their hair is wavy and long.

  C. They are teachers.

  D. They are brother and sister.

Unit 2 Test

🔘 LISTENING I

(Track 8) Look at the pictures and listen. What is the correct answer: A, B, or C?

1.

A

B

C

2.

A

B

C

LISTENING II

(Track 9) **Listen to the question and three answers. What is the correct answer: A, B, or C?**

3. A. Yes, I call them.

    B. I call them a few times a month.

    C. I have a lot of friends.

4. A. Tell me about your family.

    B. I don't have a very big family.

    C. No, they don't. They live in China.

(Track 10) **Listen to the conversation. Then listen to the question and three answers. What is the correct answer: A, B, or C?**

5. A. six kids

    B. three kids

    C. no kids

6. A. the woman's niece

    B. the woman's daughter

    C. the man's niece

GRAMMAR

Complete each conversation. What is the correct answer: A, B, or C?

7. **A:** I _____ a large family.
   B: Oh, really?

   A. doesn't have
   B. haven't
   C. don't have

8. **A:** Michael works at Karen's Restaurant.
   B: My brother _____.

   A. don't work
   B. does, too
   C. don't, either

9. **A:** Carlos _____ in Mexico City.
   B: That's great! It's beautiful there.

   A. lives
   B: live
   C. don't live

10. **A:** I don't live in San Diego.
    B: I _____. I live in Los Angeles.

    A. do, too
    B. doesn't, either
    C. don't, either

11. **A:** _____ you see your grandparents?
    B: About once a week.

    A. How does
    B. How often do
    C. Where does

12. **A:** Do Nelson and Sergio work on weekends?
    B: No, they _____.

    A. do
    B. doesn't
    C. don't

13. **A:** My aunt _____ in the White House.
    B: Oh, that's interesting!

    A. works
    B. work
    C. don't work

14. **A:** My grandparents have a house in Florida.
    B: My grandparents _____!

    A. do, too
    B. have
    C. don't have

15. **A:** Does Matt have uncles?
    B: Yes, _____.

    A. he does
    B. he doesn't
    C. they do

16. **A:** Arturo _____ in Caracas.
    B: Oh, yeah? Where does he live?

    A. don't live
    B. doesn't live
    C. live

17. **A:** Mohammed's father-in-law doesn't have a job.
    B: I know. His mother-in-law _____.

    A. do, too
    B. doesn't, either
    C. does, too

18. **A:** Does your fiancé work in an office?
    B: No. He _____ in an office. He works in a factory.

    A. works
    B. don't work
    C. doesn't work

19. **A:** _____ any grandsons?
    B: Yes, I have four.

    A. Do you
    B. You have
    C. Do you have

20. **A:** My sister doesn't have any children.
    B: My sister _____.

    A. she doesn't
    B. doesn't, either
    C. does, too

21. **A:** _____ live?
    B: They live in California.

    A. Do your parents
    B. Where do your parents
    C. How often do your parents

VOCABULARY

Read. What is the correct answer: A, B, C, or D?

22. They are Katie's parents.

   A. Emily and Douglas

   B. Sarah and Brad

   C. Brian and Michelle

   D. James and Grace

23. This is Sarah's husband.

   A. Brad

   B. Douglas

   C. Brian

   D. James

24. Who is James's cousin?

   A. Katie

   B. Grace

   C. Brad

   D. Douglas

25. Who are Emily's granddaughters?

   A. Michelle and Sarah

   B. Katie and James

   C. Katie and Grace

   D. Sarah and Grace

LIFE SKILLS

Read. What is the correct answer: A, B, C, or D?

Extra Mailing Services

Certificate of Mailing
You get a receipt to show you mailed the item on a certain date.

Delivery Confirmation
You can find out when your package is delivered.

Certified Mail
You get a receipt to show you mailed the item. You can find out when the item is delivered and who signs for it.

Insurance
If your package is lost or damaged, you get money back.

Registered Mail
You get a receipt to show you mailed the item. Your item is both certified and insured.

COD (Collect on Delivery)
The person who receives the item pays for the cost of mailing.

26. I need to know who signs for my package.

    A. Certificate of Mailing

    B. Delivery Confirmation

    C. Certified Mail

    D. Registered Mail

27. I want to know when my package is delivered.

    A. Certificate of Mailing

    B. Delivery Confirmation

    C. Insurance

    D. Registered Mail

Read. What is the correct answer: A, B, C, or D?

SERVICE	PACKAGE or LETTER	SPEED	SERVICE	PACKAGE or LETTER	SPEED
Express Mail	70 pounds or less	1–2 days	First-Class Mail	13 ounces or less	1–3 days
Priority Mail	70 pounds or less	1–3 days	Parcel Post	70 pounds or less	2–9 days

28. You want to send a 50-pound box in 1 to 2 days.

    A. Express Mail

    B. Priority Mail

    C. First-class Mail

    D. Parcel Post

29. You want to send a 12-pound mailing tube in a week.

    A. Express Mail

    B. Priority Mail

    C. First-class Mail

    D. Parcel Post

Read. What is the correct answer: A, B, C, or D?

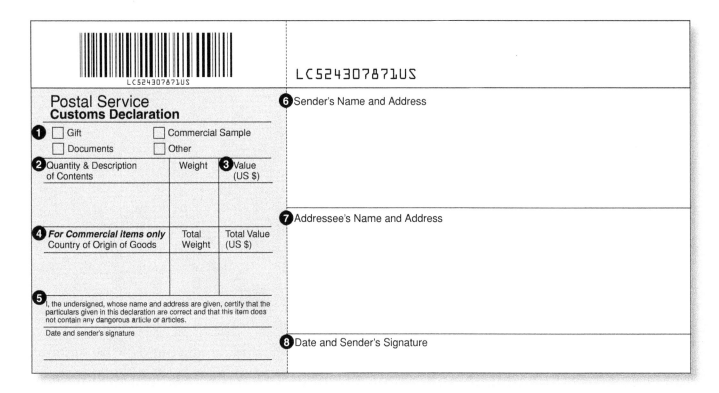

30. You want to send a package to Vietnam. Where do you write your address?

    A. ②

    B. ③

    C. ⑥

    D. ⑦

31. Where do you write about what is in the package?

    A. ① and ②

    B. ③ and ⑤

    C. ⑤ and ⑥

    D. ⑦ and ⑧

READING

Read. What is the correct answer: A, B, C, or D?

Benny and Estela are married. Benny and Estela are from the Philippines, but they live in the United States. They have one son and one daughter. Benny's family lives in the Philippines, and Estela's family does, too. Estela visits her parents once a year, but Benny doesn't visit his parents. He calls his parents on holidays.

32. What do Benny and Estela have?

   A. two sons

   B. two daughters

   C. a son and a daughter

   D. two sons and a daughter

33. How often does Benny call his parents?

   A. never

   B. a lot

   C. once a year

   D. on holidays

Unit 3 Test

LISTENING I

(Track 11) Look at the pictures and listen. What is the correct answer: A, B, or C?

1.

A

B

C

2.

A

B

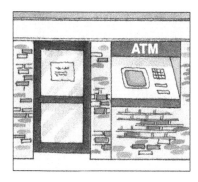

C

LISTENING II

(Track 12) **Listen to the question and three answers. What is the correct answer: A, B, or C?**

3. A. Where do you like to shop?

    B. I need to go to the ATM.

    C. Sure. I'm going to the mall tomorrow.

4. A. I need new gloves.

    B. The zipper is broken.

    C. I'm going to stop at the supermarket.

(Track 13) **Listen to the conversation. Then listen to the question and three answers. What is the correct answer: A, B, or C?**

5. A. She's going to relax.

    B. She's going to stop at the pharmacy.

    C. She's going to the bank and the laundromat.

6. A. cold

    B. hot

    C. cool

LIFE SKILLS I

(Track 14) **Look at the picture and listen. What is the correct answer: A, B, or C?**

7.

◆ MAYFIELD ◆	
DEPARTMENT STORE	
07/25/10	
Men's Accessories	
1 sunglasses	$40.00
Discount 20%	-8.00
Subtotal	$32.00
FL Sales Tax 6%	1.92
Total	$33.92
CASH	$40.00
Change	6.08

A

◆ MAYFIELD ◆	
DEPARTMENT STORE	
07/26/10	
Men's Accessories	
1 sunglasses	$40.00
Discount 25%	-10.00
Subtotal	$30.00
FL Sales Tax 6%	1.80
Total	$31.80
CASH	$32.00
Change	.20

B

◆ MAYFIELD ◆	
DEPARTMENT STORE	
07/27/10	
Men's Accessories	
1 sunglasses	$40.00
Discount 30%	-12.00
Subtotal	$28.00
FL Sales Tax 6%	1.68
Total	$29.68
CASH	$30.00
Change	.32

C

GRAMMAR

Complete each conversation. What is the correct answer: A, B, or C?

8. **A:** Jorge _____ a jacket for work.
   B: Oh, there's a sale at Mayfield's.

   A. to buy
   B. needs to buy
   C. don't need to buy

9. **A:** Kelly _____ that hat.
   B: Why? What's wrong with it?

   A. exchange
   B. wants to exchange
   C. don't want to exchange

10. **A:** My new pants are perfect!
    B: OK, then you _____ to return them.

    A. don't need
    B. doesn't need
    C. needs

11. **A:** I'm going to buy that sweater.
    B: Good idea. It's _____ pretty!

    A. very
    B. too
    C. not

12. **A:** My kids _____ shop at the big sale tomorrow.
    B: Oh, really?

    A. going to
    B. aren't going
    C. aren't going to

13. **A:** What are your plans for tonight?
    B: We _____ return the movie to the video store.

    A. 're going
    B. going to
    C. are going to

14. **A:** Where is Yun-fat going?
    B: He's _____ a raincoat and umbrella.

    A. going to
    B. going to buy
    C. to buy

15. A: Do you need to work next week?

B: No. We_____ work next week.

    A. 're not going to

    B. not going to

    C. are going

16. A: Those are nice pants.

B: Yes, but they are _____ expensive. They cost $50, and I only have $40.

    A. very

    B. too

    C. not

17. A: My brother isn't going to run any errands on Saturday.

B: Good. He's _____ have time to relax.

    A. not going

    B. going to

    C. going

18. A: That scarf is _____ colorful!

B: I know. Do you want to buy it for Tumba?

    A. a lot

    B. very

    C. too

19. A: Bao _____ to the store with us. He wants to watch TV at home.

B: OK, fine.

    A. doesn't come

    B. want to come

    C. doesn't want to come

20. A: I like your new coat.

B: Thanks, but it's _____ big. I'm going to exchange it for a smaller size.

    A. a lot

    B. very

    C. too

21. A: Your new boots are really colorful.

B: I know. I think they're *too* colorful! I _____ them.

    A. exchanges

    B. want to exchange

    C. doesn't want to exchange

22. A: This swimsuit is _____ pretty.

B: I know. It's expensive, too!

    A. very

    B. a lot

    C. too

VOCABULARY

Read. What is the correct answer: A, B, C, or D?

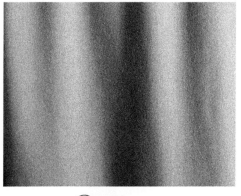

① cotton

② denim

③ vinyl

④ nylon

23. What are jeans made of?

   A. ①

   B. ②

   C. ③

   D. ④

24. What are windbreakers made of?

   A. ①

   B. ②

   C. ③

   D. ④

Read. What is the correct answer: A, B, C, or D?

1

2

3

4

25. My scarf is made of silk.
    A. ①
    B. ②
    C. ③
    D. ④

26. Mom's new boots are made of leather.
    A. ①
    B. ②
    C. ③
    D. ④

LIFE SKILLS II

Read. What is the correct answer: A, B, C, or D?

27. What's the name of the clothing store?

    A. One-Day Sale!

    B. Women's

    C. Men's

    D. Metro Mart

28. What is on sale?

    A. dresses, skirts, and hats

    B. dresses, shoes, and blouses

    C. dresses, hats, and jackets

    D. dresses, jackets, and shirts

29. What is the sale price on the women's dresses?

    A. $45.99

    B. $36.99

    C. $5.00

    D. $59.99

Read. What is the correct answer: A, B, C, or D?

David Camacho
123 Appleton St.
Miami, FL 33121

101

November 1, 2007

PAY TO THE
ORDER OF ___Union Gas_____ $ | 246.23 |

Two Hundred Forty-six and ²³/₁₀₀ —————————— DOLLARS

ELM BANK
49-22 Victor Street
Miami, FL 33125

FOR ____Acc. #624135____   _____David Camacho_____

4:3788825424: 3|||971335|||01

---

30. This check is for _____.

A. David Camacho

B. Elm Bank

C. Miami, FL

D. Union Gas

31. The amount of the check is _____.

A. 101

B. 246.23

C. 1234

D. 624135

READING

Read. What is the correct answer: A, B, C, or D?

Elena is going to exchange a shirt. It's too small for her son. It's very expensive. She doesn't want to spend more money. Elena needs to show her receipt to the sales assistant. Then she is going to get a new shirt in a size 12 for her son.

32. Why does Elena want to exchange the shirt?

A. It's too big.

B. It's too small.

C. It's a size 12.

D. She wants to spend more money.

33. What does Elena need to do?

A. She needs to spend more money.

B. She needs to buy a smaller shirt.

C. She needs to show her receipt.

D. She needs to buy a cheaper shirt.

Unit 4 Test

LISTENING I

(Track 15) Look at the pictures and listen. What is the correct answer: A, B, or C?

1.

A

B

C

2.

A

B

C

LISTENING II

(Track 16) Listen to the question and three answers. What is the correct answer: A, B, or C?

3. A. Sounds like fun.

   B. What about you?

   C. They're going for a bike ride.

4. A. Sorry, I can't.

   B. I really hate to get up early.

   C. Really?

(Track 17) Listen to the conversation. Then listen to the question and three answers. What is the correct answer: A, B, or C?

5. A. The woman has to work.

   B. The woman doesn't feel well.

   C. The woman has other plans.

6. A. He's going to a computer class.

   B. He's going out to eat with his family.

   C. He's going to a karate class.

GRAMMAR

Complete each conversation. What is the correct answer: A, B, or C?

7. **A:** How often does your aunt go to the beach?
   B: She goes _____ Saturday.

   A. every
   B. once a week
   C. never

8. **A:** I _____ out to eat.
   B: I do, too!

   A. loves to go
   B. love to go
   C. to go

9. **A:** My sister _____ at the hospital tonight.
   B: Really? She works a lot!

   A. have to work
   B. don't have to work
   C. has to work

10. **A:** How often does Martin jog?
    B: He jogs _____.

    A. hardly ever
    B. once
    C. twice a week

11. **A:** The Parks like to go to the beach.
    B: I know. They _____ on the weekends.

    A. sometimes
    B. usually go
    C. hardly ever goes

12. **A:** We have to work late on Saturday nights.
    B: Oh, really? I _____ work on Saturdays. I work on Sundays.

    A. doesn't have to
    B. don't have to
    C. do have to

13. **A:** Pavel _____ to go to the zoo.
    B: No, he doesn't.

    A. don't like
    B. love
    C. doesn't like

14. A: My parents live near the beach, but they _____ go swimming.

 B: Why? Are they afraid of the water?

   A. often

   B. never

   C. always

15. A: We _____ go to the video store on Friday night.

 B: Yeah, I do, too. I watch a video every weekend!

   A. never

   B. always

   C. hardly ever

16. A: I like to go jogging.

 B: I don't. I _____ hiking.

   A. likes to go

   B. like to go

   C. doesn't like to go

17. A: My children love to fish.

 B: My children _____. They like to have loud parties!

   A. don't like to fish

   B. doesn't like to fish

   C. does like to fish

18. A: How often _____?

 B: Every day.

   A. does your cousin

   B. your cousin plays soccer

   C. does your cousin play soccer

19. A: Jorani _____ does her English homework.

 B: Yes. She is a really good student.

   A. once a month

   B. never

   C. always

20. A: Chico _____ get up early tomorrow.

 B: I know. He has the day off.

   A. have to

   B. doesn't have to

   C. has

21. A: Greg has to go to a concert at school tonight.

 B: I know. I _____ to that concert, too!

   A. have to go

   B. have

   C. has to go

VOCABULARY

Read. What is the correct answer: A, B, C, or D?

①

②

③

④

22. My brother loves to go jogging, but I hate it.

   A. ①

   B. ②

   C. ③

   D. ④

23. Su-Jin likes to go hiking.

   A. ①

   B. ②

   C. ③

   D. ④

Read. What is the correct answer: A, B, C, or D?

①

②

③

④

24. My wife and I go dancing every Saturday night.

    A. ①

    B. ②

    C. ③

    D. ④

25. Sunday is a good day to go for a bike ride.

    A. ①

    B. ②

    C. ③

    D. ④

LIFE SKILLS

Read. What is the correct answer: A, B, C, or D?

EastWindsor June
Community Center Calendar

Sunday	Monday	Tuesday	Wednesday	Thursday	Friday	Saturday
	1 7:00 – 9:00 P.M. ESL class	2 9:00 – 10:00 A.M. exercise class	3 7:00 – 9:00 P.M. ESL class	4 9:00 – 10:00 A.M. exercise class	5 8:00 P.M. movie club	6 1:00 – 4:00 P.M. swim team
7 8:00 A.M.– 4:00 P.M. hiking club	8 7:00 – 9:00 P.M. ESL class	9 9:00 – 10:00 A.M. exercise class	10 7:00 – 9:00 P.M. ESL class	11 9:00 – 10:00 A.M. exercise class	12 8:00 – 10:00 P.M. dance class	13 1:00 – 4:00 P.M. swim team

26. When does the movie club meet?

A. every Monday

B. every Friday

C. from 7:00 to 9:00 P.M.

D. on the first Friday of the month

27. How often does the ESL class meet?

A. once a month

B. once a week

C. twice a week

D. three times a week

Read. What is the correct answer: A, B, C, or D?

Greenville Community Center Calendar — September

Sunday	Monday	Tuesday	Wednesday	Thursday	Friday	Saturday
		1 Computer class 10 A.M. – 12:00 P.M.	2	3 Computer class 10 A.M. – 12:00 P.M.	4 Guitar class 6:00 – 7:30 P.M.	5 Concert at the zoo 1:00 – 2:00 P.M.
6 Biking club 1:00 – 5:00 P.M.	7	8 Computer class 10 A.M. – 12:00 P.M.	9	10 Computer class 10 A.M. – 12:00 P.M.	11 Guitar class 6:00 – 7:30 P.M.	12

28. When does the guitar class meet?

A. every Friday

B. twice a week

C. from 6:00 to 8:00 P.M.

D. every Monday and Wednesday

29. When does the computer class meet?

A. on Wednesdays

B. every Saturday

C. every day at 10 A.M.

D. every Tuesday and Thursday morning

30. When is the concert at the zoo?

A. from 10:00 A.M. to 12:00 P.M.

B. the first Saturday of the month

C. every Saturday

D. on Saturdays and Sundays

READING

Read. What is the correct answer: A, B, C, or D?

Mark and Alisa love to go dancing. They go dancing every Friday night. They also like to go for a bike ride on Saturday mornings. They go for a walk in the park twice a week. They hardly ever go swimming. Mark doesn't like to go jogging. Alisa likes to go jogging, but she hates to go fishing.

31. What do Alisa and Mark both love to do?

    A. go jogging

    B. go dancing

    C. go shopping

    D. go swimming

32. How often do they go for a walk?

    A. every night

    B. Friday night

    C. every Saturday

    D. twice a week

33. What does Alisa hate to do?

    A. go for a bike ride

    B. go for a walk

    C. go jogging

    D. go fishing

Unit 5 Test

(Track 18) Look at the pictures and listen. What is the correct answer: A, B, or C?

1.

A   B   C

2.

A   B   C

🖸 LISTENING II

(Track 19) **Listen to the question and three answers. What is the correct answer: A, B, or C?**

3. A. Sure. No problem.

   B. Is there a park nearby?

   C. You should call the building manager.

4. A. Yes, there is.

   B. Sure. It has three bedrooms.

   C. Oh, good.

(Track 20) **Listen to the conversation. Then listen to the question and three answers. What is the correct answer: A, B, or C?**

5. A. There's no parking lot.

   B. There's no free parking on the street.

   C. There's no parking lot, and there isn't any free parking on the street.

6. A. It's on First Street.

   B. It's on Second Street near the gas station.

   C. It's on the right near the pharmacy.

GRAMMAR

Complete each conversation. What is the correct answer: A, B, or C?

7. **A:** The refrigerator _____.
   B: You should call the building manager.

   A. working
   B. aren't working
   C. isn't working

8. **A:** The lock is broken.
   B: I know. The locksmith _____ it right now.

   A. is fixing
   B. fixing
   C. are fixing

9. **A:** The faucets _____ again.
   B: Oh, no!

   A. is leaking
   B. are leaking
   C. isn't leaking

10. **A:** Is there a restaurant near the apartment?
    B: No, _____.

    A. there is
    B. there aren't
    C. there isn't

11. **A:** How many bathrooms _____?
    B: There are three.

    A. are there
    B. there are
    C. is there

12. **A:** Is there a park near the apartment?
    B: No. _____ parks in the neighborhood.

    A. There isn't
    B. There are no
    C. Are there any

13. **A:** _____ a lot of families with children on this street.
    B: That's great! I love kids.

    A. There is
    B. There isn't
    C. There are

14. A: Can I use that washing machine?

B: Sorry, no. It _____.

    A. isn't working

    B. aren't working

    C. not working

15. A: _____ a lot of supermarkets near here?

B: Yes, there are three.

    A. Are there

    B. Is there

    C. How many

16. A: How many windows are in the laundry room?

B: _____ windows.

    A. Are there any

    B. There is no

    C. There aren't any

17. A: Is your toilet clogged?

B: Yes. We _____ for the plumber to fix it.

    A. am waiting

    B. is waiting

    C. are waiting

18. A: Is there a lot of traffic on Park Avenue?

B: Yes, _____.

    A. there are

    B. there isn't

    C. there is

19. A: The lights _____. Maya is calling the electrician now.

B: Good.

    A. is working

    B. isn't working

    C. aren't working

20. A: Is the bus stop far from the house?

B: No. _____ a bus stop nearby.

    A. There's

    B. There aren't

    C. There are

21. A: Are there a lot of closets in your new apartment?

B: _____. There's only one.

    A. Yes, there are

    B. No, there isn't

    C. No, there aren't

VOCABULARY

Read. What is the correct answer: A, B, C, or D?

Maria

Alfredo

22. What's Maria's problem?

    A. Her faucet is leaking.

    B. Her toilet is clogged.

    C. Her sink is clogged.

    D. There's no hot water.

23. What's Alfredo's problem?

    A. His mailbox is broken.

    B. His window is stuck.

    C. His stove isn't working.

    D. His door is stuck.

Read. What is the correct answer: A, B, C, or D?

①

②

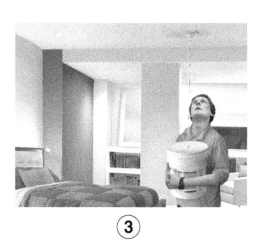

③

④

24. There's no hot water.

    A. ①

    B. ②

    C. ③

    D. ④

25. The washing machine isn't working.

    A. ①

    B. ②

    C. ③

    D. ④

LIFE SKILLS

Read. What is the correct answer: A, B, C, or D?

> **Beach**. 2 BR, LR,
> util. incl. Nr. trans.
> No pets. $1,250/mo.,
> sec. dep. $1,000.
> Call Jen (207) 111-0099

26. Where is the apartment?

A. far from the beach

B. near transportation

C. near schools

D. near shopping

27. What does the apartment have?

A. three bedrooms

B. a living room

C. a laundry room

D. two bathrooms

28. How much does the tenant have to pay?

A. $1,200 for rent + utilities

B. $1,250 for rent + no security deposit

C. $1,250 for rent + $1,000 for a security deposit

D. $1,000 for rent + utilities

Read. What is the correct answer: A, B, C, or D?

South End. Large 2 BR, LR, EIK, 2 BA. W/D. Ht. + hw. not incl. Pets allowed. No fee. $1,200/mo. 1 mo. sec. dep. Available immediately. Call Rick 207-555-1212.

①

Downtown. Sunny furn. 1 BR apt. A/C. Pkg. garage. Nr. trans. Pets OK. $950/mo. Util. incl. No fee. City Properties 207-555-8765.

②

North Square. Nice 2 BR, LR, DR. No pets. $1,200/mo. Ht. hw. incl. Nr. schools. Fee + 2 mo. sec. dep. Maven Realty 207-555-9989.

③

Beach. 2 BR, LR, util. incl. Nr. trans. No pets. $1,250/mo., sec. dep. $1,000. Call Jen (207) 111-0099

④

29. Igor can spend $1,000 a month on rent. Which apartment is best for him?
   A. ①
   B. ②
   C. ③
   D. ④

30. Claude and Sandrine work near North Square, and they have one child. Which apartment is best for them?
   A. ①
   B. ②
   C. ③
   D. ④

31. Solange loves the beach. Which apartment is best for her?
   A. ①
   B. ②
   C. ③
   D. ④

READING

Read. What is the correct answer: A, B, C, or D?

Mia needs an apartment. She reads the newspaper apartment ads. She goes to look at an apartment with two bedrooms. There isn't a bus stop in the neighborhood, but there are two restaurants nearby. The hot water isn't working and the bathroom door is stuck. But a plumber is fixing the hot water, and the building manager is fixing the bathroom door. Mia can move in next week.

32. What is near the apartment?

    A. a bus stop

    B. a park

    C. two restaurants

    D. a laundromat

33. What problem is the building manager fixing?

    A. There's no bus stop.

    B. There's no air conditioning.

    C. The hot water isn't working.

    D. The bathroom door is stuck.

Unit 6 Test

🔘 LISTENING I

(Track 21) **Look at the pictures and listen. What is the correct answer: A, B, or C?**

1.

A	B	C

2.

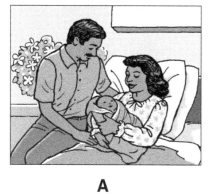

A	B	C

🖸 LISTENING II

(Track 22) **Listen to the question and three answers. What is the correct answer: A, B, or C?**

3. A. Sounds great!

    B. It was really nice, thanks.

    C. How was the family reunion?

4. A. I always wanted to be an actor.

    B. I got married five years ago.

    C. Yes, I did, but I didn't practice speaking a lot.

(Track 23) **Listen to the conversation. Then listen to the question and three answers. What is the correct answer: A, B, or C?**

5. A. She was late to work.

    B. She took the wrong train.

    C. She overslept.

6. A. He watched old movies with his aunts and uncles.

    B. He danced all night.

    C. He played games.

LIFE SKILLS I

(Track 24) **Look at the pictures and listen. What is the correct answer: A, B, or C?**

7.

February						
Sun	Mon	Tues	Wed	Thu	Fri	Sat
					1	2
3	4	5	6	7	8	9
10	11	12	13	14	15	16
17	18	19	20	21	22	23
24	25	26	27	28	29	

May						
Sun	Mon	Tues	Wed	Thu	Fri	Sat
				1	2	3
4	5	6	7	8	9	10
11	12	13	14	15	16	17
18	19	20	21	22	23	24
25	26	27	28	29	30	31

December						
Sun	Mon	Tues	Wed	Thu	Fri	Sat
	1	2	3	4	5	6
7	8	9	10	11	12	13
14	15	16	17	18	19	20
21	22	23	24	25	26	27
28	29	30	31			

A   **B**   **C**

8.

January						
Sun	Mon	Tues	Wed	Thu	Fri	Sat
		1	2	3	4	5
6	7	8	9	10	11	12
13	14	15	16	17	18	19
20	21	22	23	24	25	26
27	28	29	30	31		

July						
Sun	Mon	Tues	Wed	Thu	Fri	Sat
		1	2	3	4	5
6	7	8	9	10	11	12
13	14	15	16	17	18	19
20	21	22	23	24	25	26
27	28	29	30	31		

November						
Sun	Mon	Tues	Wed	Thu	Fri	Sat
						1
2	3	4	5	6	7	8
9	10	11	12	13	14	15
16	17	18	19	20	21	22
23 30	24	25	26	27	28	29

A   **B**   **C**

GRAMMAR

Complete each conversation. What is the correct answer: A, B, or C?

9. **A:** Did you grow up in Long Beach?

    B: Yes, _____.

    A. I grew up

    B. I didn't

    C. I did

10. **A:** I _____ to the United States in 1978.

    B: Oh. We didn't come until 1997.

    A. come

    B. came

    C. comes

11. **A:** Did you meet your wife in the United States?

    B: No. I _____ her in this country. I met her in Korea.

    A. didn't meet

    B. don't meet

    C. not meet

12. **A:** Did Angelica and Andres enjoy their trip to Florida?

    B: They _____ Florida. They went to California.

    A. doesn't visit

    B. didn't visit

    C. visits

13. **A:** Did Ms. Cong get a new job?

    B: No, she _____.

    A. did

    B. did not get

    C. didn't

14. **A:** _____ Kevin get to his English class this morning?

    B: He got to class at 10:30 A.M.

    A. When

    B. When did

    C. Why did

15. **A:** _____ to Kingman?

    B: No, they didn't.

    A. They moved

    B. Did they

    C. Did they move

16. **A:** Michael _____ at photos with his family last night.
    B: That sounds fun.

    A. looked
    B. look
    C. looks

17. **A:** What time did she get to work yesterday?
    B: At 11 A.M. She _____ in traffic.

    A. got stuck
    B. gets stuck
    C. get stuck

18. **A:** _____ do last weekend?
    B: She went to a birthday party.

    A. What does Natalia
    B. Did Natalia
    C. What did Natalia

19. **A:** _____ Achmed miss the train this morning?
    B: He missed the train because he forgot his wallet.

    A. When did
    B. Why did
    C. What time did

20. **A:** I _____ in Colombia.
    B: Oh, really? Where did you grow up?

    A. don't grow up
    B. not grow up
    C. didn't grow up

21. **A:** Did you get up early this morning?
    B: Yes, _____.

    A. you did
    B. I did
    C. I didn't

22. **A:** The party last weekend was great. Everyone _____ all night.
    B: That sounds like fun!

    A. dances
    B. danced
    C. dance

23. **A:** Did you finish your homework last night?
    B: No. I _____ it because I was sick.

    A. didn't finish
    B. finished
    C. don't finish

VOCABULARY

Read. What is the correct answer: A, B, C, or D?

24. We are going to my sister's potluck dinner.
    A. ①
    B. ②
    C. ③
    D. ④

25. Ted's retirement party is tonight.
    A. ①
    B. ②
    C. ③
    D. ④

Read. What is the correct answer: A, B, C, or D?

Veronica

Anita

26. What did Veronica do last week?

A. She had a graduation party.

B. She had a birthday party.

C. She had a holiday meal.

D. She had a family reunion.

27. Where is Anita in the picture?

A. She is at her anniversary party.

B. She is at a funeral.

C. She is at her wedding.

D. She is at a surprise party.

LIFE SKILLS II

Read. What is the correct answer: A, B, C, or D?

January

Sun	Mon	Tues	Wed	Thu	Fri	Sat
		1	2	3	4	5
6	7	8	9	10	11	12
13	14	15	16	17	18	19
20	21	22	23	24	25	26
27	28	29	30	31		

①

July

Sun	Mon	Tues	Wed	Thu	Fri	Sat
		1	2	3	4	5
6	7	8	9	10	11	12
13	14	15	16	17	18	19
20	21	22	23	24	25	26
27	28	29	30	31		

②

September

Sun	Mon	Tues	Wed	Thu	Fri	Sat
	1	2	3	4	5	6
7	8	9	10	11	12	13
14	15	16	17	18	19	20
21	22	23	24	25	26	27
28	29	30				

③

October

Sun	Mon	Tues	Wed	Thu	Fri	Sat
			1	2	3	4
5	6	7	8	9	10	11
12	13	14	15	16	17	18
19	20	21	22	23	24	25
26	27	28	29	30	31	

④

28. Labor Day is in this month.
- A. ①
- B. ②
- C. ③
- D. ④

29. Martin Luther King Jr. Day is in this month.
- A. ①
- B. ②
- C. ③
- D. ④

Read. What is the correct answer: A, B, C, or D?

May 10, 2007

Dear Ms. Sato,

My son, Alberto Morales, was absent from school last week because he was sick. He is feeling better today. Please allow him to return to class.

Sincerely,

Sonia Morales

30. Who wrote the note?

A. Alberto Morales

B. Alberto's teacher

C. Alberto's mother

D. Alberto's grandmother

31. Why did the person write the note?

A. Alberto was absent from school last week.

B. Alberto is absent from school today.

C. Alberto is sick today.

D. Alberto's mother is sick today.

READING

What is the correct answer: A, B, C, or D?

This is a picture of Janay and Fabio at their wedding. The wedding was in Miami, Florida. Janay was born in the United States. She grew up in New Orleans. Fabio came to the United States from Brazil in 2001. He was 25 years old. Fabio and Janay met in college in 2002. They both graduated from college in 2004. They got married in 2006.

32. Where did Fabio grow up?

A. in Miami

B. in New Orleans

C. in Brazil

D. in college

33. When was Janay and Fabio's wedding?

A. in 2001

B. in 2003

C. in 2004

D. in 2006

Unit 7 Test

💿 LISTENING I

(Track 25) **Look at the pictures and listen. What is the correct answer: A, B, or C?**

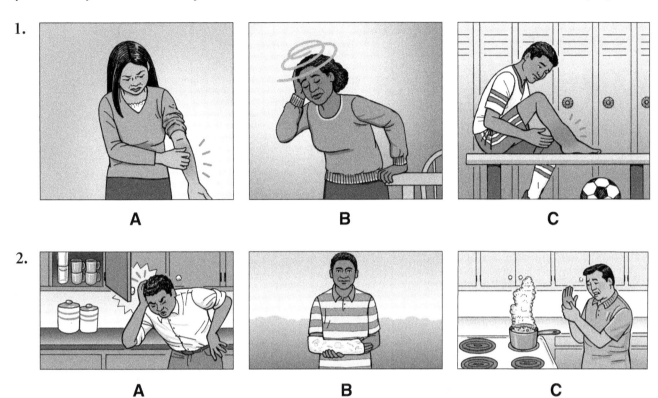

1.

    A   **B**   **C**

2.

    A   **B**   **C**

LISTENING II

(Track 26) **Listen to the question and three answers. What is the correct answer: A, B, or C?**

3. A. What's the matter?

    B. My throat is swollen.

    C. Yes, that's fine.

4. A. I'm nauseous.

    B. I have an appointment at 2:30.

    C. I'm sorry to hear that.

(Track 27) **Listen to the conversation. Then listen to the question and three answers. What is the correct answer: A, B, or C?**

5. A. The man is sick.

    B. The woman has an earache.

    C. The man's daughter has an earache.

6. A. She burned her hand.

    B. She sprained her wrist.

    C. She fell and broke her arm.

GRAMMAR

Complete each conversation. What is the correct answer: A, B, or C?

7. **A:** My son _____ a sore throat yesterday.
   B: That's too bad.

   A. have
   B. has
   C. had

8. **A:** I need to make an appointment tomorrow morning, please.
   B: OK. Dr. De Souza has an opening _____ 8 A.M.

   A. on
   B. at
   C. from

9. **A:** The doctor's office is open _____ 8 A.M. to 5 P.M.
   B: OK.

   A. from
   B. at
   C. on

10. **A:** Marco had an accident last night. He _____ his ankle!
    B: Sorry to hear that.

    A. break
    B. breaks
    C. broke

11. **A:** Your appointment is at 9 A.M. tomorrow. Please arrive _____ 8:45 because
    you need to fill out some forms before the appointment.
    B: OK.

    A. by
    B. in
    C. on

12. **A:** What are you doing here in the emergency room?
    B: I _____ my hand at work this morning.

    A. cuts
    B. cut
    C. hurts

13. **A:** Is your office open _____ Thursday night?
    B: Yes, we are open until 8 P.M.

    A. on
    B. at
    C. by

14. **A:** I'm going to the pharmacy _____ my cold medicine now.
    B: OK. See you later.

    A. because
    B. for
    C. from

15. **A:** Dina went to the hospital _____ she had chest pains.
    B: Oh, I'm sorry to hear that!

    A. for
    B. in
    C. because

16. **A:** What's the matter with Admassu?
    B: He _____ in the shower and sprained his ankle.

    A. fell
    B. fall
    C. falls

17. **A:** I have a question for the doctor.
    B: OK, but he's busy right now. He'll call you back _____ about half an hour.

    A. by
    B. from
    C. in

18. **A:** I'm leaving early _____ I have a dental appointment.
    B: OK, see you tomorrow.

    A. because
    B. for
    C. to

19. **A:** Ivan _____ hurt in the soccer game yesterday.
    B: Oh, no!

    A. hurts
    B. get
    C. got

20. **A:** Can you come in _____ a check up at 1 P.M. on Friday?
    B: Yes, that's fine.

    A. because
    B. for
    C. in

21. **A:** Did Young Sun go to school yesterday?
    B: No. She was absent _____ she had a fever.

    A. from
    B. for
    C. because

VOCABULARY

Read. What is the correct answer: A, B, C, or D?

1

2

3

4

22. I have a stiff neck.

   A. ①

   B. ②

   C. ③

   D. ④

23. I have a sore throat.

   A. ①

   B. ②

   C. ③

   D. ④

Read. What is the correct answer: A, B, C, or D?

Eduardo

Sergei

24. What's the matter with Eduardo?

    A. He has an upset stomach.

    B. He has a fever.

    C. He has heartburn.

    D. He has diarrhea.

25. What's the matter with Sergei?

    A. He has a headache.

    B. He has the chills.

    C. He has a cough.

    D. He has a headache.

LIFE SKILLS

Read. What is the correct answer: A, B, C, or D?

Tams Extra Strength Antacid

Active Ingredient: calcium carbonate 750 mg

Uses: Relieves
- Upset stomach
- Heartburn

Directions:
- Chew 2–4 tablets as needed
- Do not take more than 10 tablets in 24 hours
- Children under 6: Do not use this extra-strength product

Expiration date: 5/11

26. What is this medicine for?

A. headache

B. heartburn

C. cough

D. sore throat

27. How much of this medicine can people take?

A. 2 tablets every day

B. 4 tablets every day

C. more than 10 tablets in 24 hours

D. not more than 10 tablets in 24 hours

28. Who cannot use this medicine?

A. children under 6

B. adults and children

C. adults

D. children over 6

Read. What is the correct answer: A, B, C, or D?

RX: 222253
Wally's Pharmacy

Doctor: Alice Che   **Patient:** Jerry Mixer

Dosage: Take 1 tablet every 3 hours
as needed for pain.
Take with food.
May cause dizziness.
May cause drowsiness.

Acetaminophen with codeine

1 Refill   **Exp:** 03-08-10

29. Who is this medicine for?

A. Alice Che

B. Jerry Mixer

C. Wally's Pharmacy

D. acetaminophen with codeine

30. What is the dosage for the medicine?

A. 1 tablet every day

B. 3 tablets every day

C. 1 tablet every 3 hours

D. 3 tablets every hour

31. What is the expiration date?

A. There is no expiration date.

B. March 8, 2010

C. one refill

D. every 3 hours

READING

Read. What is the correct answer: A, B, C, or D?

Susana had a car accident on Monday morning. She made an appointment with the doctor on Tuesday because she had a bad headache. She hurt her elbow, too. She got a prescription from the doctor. Then she went to the pharmacy to get medicine for her pain. Susana feels better now. She thinks she can go back to work on Friday.

32. What was the matter with Susana?

A. She had the flu.

B. She had a bad headache.

C. She had a sore throat.

D. She had a fever.

33. Where did Susana go after her appointment?

A. She went back to work.

B. She went home.

C. She went to the pharmacy to see the doctor.

D. She went to the pharmacy to get medicine.

Unit 8 Test

 LISTENING I

(Track 28) Look at the pictures and listen. What is the correct answer: A, B, or C?

1.

      A   **B**   **C**

2.

      A   **B**   **C**

LISTENING II

(Track 29) **Listen to the question and three answers. What is the correct answer: A, B, or C?**

3. A. I prefer afternoons, but I am flexible.

    B. I came to the United States five years ago.

    C. In three weeks.

4. A. Things in my life have changed, and I'd like to do something different.

    B. I receive shipments and unload materials.

    C. No, I can't, but I can learn.

(Track 30) **Listen to the conversation. Then listen to the question and three answers. What is the correct answer: A, B, or C?**

5. A. She greets visitors.

    B. She prepares food and cleans equipment.

    C. She prepares food, but she doesn't clean equipment.

6. A. to stay at his job

    B. to work on a different schedule

    C. to find a job closer to his house

GRAMMAR

Complete each conversation. What is the correct answer: A, B, or C?

7. **A:** _____ operate a forklift?
   B: Yes, he can.

   A. Can
   B. Can Alfonso
   C. Alfonso can't

8. **A:** I can't work Friday _____ Saturday.
   B: OK.

   A. or
   B. and
   C. not

9. **A:** Pang came to the United States _____.
   B: I didn't know that.

   A. in one year
   B. two weeks
   C. five years ago

10. **A:** Can Thu and Hoa speak Chinese?
    B: No, they _____.

    A. do
    B. can
    C. can't

11. **A:** When did you get your job?
    B: I got it _____.

    A. six months
    B. the summer
    C. last year

12. **A:** Oswaldo started college _____.
    B: Oh, really? Does he like it?

    A. two weeks
    B. two weeks ago
    C. September

13. **A:** Is Abimbola flexible?
    B: Yes. He can take classes in the afternoon _____ in the evening.

    A. for
    B. and
    C. not

14. **A:** Can you sort materials?

    B: No, I _____.

    A. can't
    B. can
    C. don't

15. **A:** Leo can't use a computer _____ answer the phone.

    B: No, he can't, but he can learn.

    A. and
    B. or
    C. do

16. **A:** _____ heavy boxes?

    B: Yes, he can.

    A. Dan lifts
    B. Can Dan
    C. Can Dan lift

17. **A:** Can Carol work first shift _____ second shift?

    B: She can work the first shift. She can't work second shift.

    A. or
    B. and
    C. not

18. **A:** Paolo got a job _____.

    B: That's great!

    A. in April
    B. three months
    C. last

19. **A:** I _____ people with computer problems.

    B: Oh.

    A. cannot
    B. can't help
    C. not help

20. **A:** _____, he moved to the United States.

    B: I see.

    A. A week
    B. August
    C. One week later

21. **A:** Can you work Saturday or Sunday?

    B: Both. I can work Saturday _____ Sunday.

    A. and
    B. or
    C. in

VOCABULARY

What is the correct answer: A, B, C, or D?

①

②

①

③

22. Terry handles phone calls.

   A. ①

   B. ②

   C. ③

   D. ④

23. Dr. Fuller takes care of patients.

   A. ①

   B. ②

   C. ③

   D. ④

Read. What is the correct answer: A, B, C, or D?

Yuri

Jamila

24. What can Yuri do?

    A. He can record patient information.

    B. He can clean kitchen equipment.

    C. He can plan work schedules.

    D. He can unload materials.

25. What can Jamila do?

    A. She can install computer hardware.

    B. She can receive shipments.

    C. She can stock shelves.

    D. She can prepare food.

LIFE SKILLS

Read. What is the correct answer: A, B, C, or D?

HELP WANTED

OFFICE ASSISTANT

PT pos. M–F mornings, 9:00–12:00.
1 yr. exp. req. Need excel. tel. skills.
Bnfts. Good pay. Call Rachel for an
interview at (200) 555-5555.

26. What are the hours for the job?

A. Monday to Friday, eight hours a day

B. Monday to Friday, three hours a day

C. Monday and Friday, three hours a day

D. Monday to Friday afternoons

27. What do you need to have for this job?

A. excellent references

B. many years of experience

C. one year of experience

D. excellent computer skills

28. How can you apply for this job?

A. Send your resume.

B. Fax your resume.

C. Call for an interview.

D. Apply in person at the office.

Read. What is the correct answer: A, B, C, or D?

Super Foods Supermarket

Job Application

Personal Information

Full name _____

Address _____

❶ Phone number _____ Are you under age 18? ☐ yes ☐ no

❷ Position you are applying for: _____

Days you can work:
- ☐ Monday
- ☐ Wednesday
- ☐ Friday
- ☐ Sunday
- ☐ Tuesday
- ☐ Thursday
- ☐ Saturday

❸ Hours you can work: From _____ to _____ o'clock

❹ What day can you start work? _____

Employment History

❺ Present or last position:

Employer _____

Address _____

Supervisor _____ Phone number _____

29. Where do you write the job you want?

A. ①
B. ②
C. ③
D. ④

30. Where can you write the hours you can work?

A. ②
B. ③
C. ④
D. ⑤

31. Where do you write your last job?

A. ①
B. ②
C. ③
D. ⑤

READING

Read. What is the correct answer: A, B, C, or D?

Antonio came to the United States from Honduras eight years ago. Last fall, he started computer classes. He learned many computer skills. Now he can fix computers and install computer hardware. Antonio can also type well. Now he wants to apply for jobs. He is still a student, so he wants to work part time. He is flexible, but he prefers to work mornings. He can't work weekends.

32. What can Antonio do now?

    A. He can fix computers, but he can't type.

    B. He can fix computers and install computer hardware.

    C. He can't install computer hardware or fix computers.

    D. He can't fix computers or type.

33. When does Antonio want to work?

    A. every day for eight hours

    B. every day in the morning

    C. Monday to Friday in the morning

    D. on the weekends

Unit 9 Test

LISTENING I

(Track 31) Look at the pictures and listen. What is the correct answer: A, B, or C?

1.

        A   B   C

2.

        A   B   C

📀 LISTENING II

(Track 32) Listen to the question and three answers. What is the correct answer: A, B, or C?

3.   A. Oh, yeah? What day?

     B. That way we can both go.

     C. Let's all talk tonight after dinner.

4.   A. That's good to hear.

     B. I'll talk to him tonight.

     C. So, how's John doing?

(Track 33) Listen to the conversation. Then listen to the question and three answers. What is the correct answer: A, B, or C?

5.   A. She's getting to school on time.

     B. She's paying attention in class.

     C. She's fooling around in class.

6.   A. He needs to study more.

     B. He writes well.

     C. He has trouble with language arts.

LIFE SKILLS I

(Track 34) Look at the pictures and listen. What is the correct answer: A, B, or C?

7.

Date __11/9__ Time __1:00 P.M.__
To __Ms. Mare__

| **While You Were Out** |

From __Lindsay Bolla__
Phone __(917) 555-5454__

Message: _____
_____

A

Date __11/9__ Time __1:00 P.M.__
To __Lindsay Bolla__

| **While You Were Out** |

From __Ms. Mare__
Phone __(917) 555-5454__

Message: _____
_____

B

Date __11/9__ Time __1:00 P.M.__
To __Ms. Mare__

| **While You Were Out** |

From __Lindsay Bolla__
Phone __(917) 500-5366__

Message: _____
_____

C

8.

Date __11/9__ Time __1:30 P.M.__
To __Mr. Fong__

| **While You Were Out** |

From __Parker Sanchez__
Phone __(917) 333-5555__
Message: __call about Ricardo's
science homework__

A

Date __11/9__ Time __1:30 P.M.__
To __Mr. Sanchez__

| **While You Were Out** |

From __Parker Fong__
Phone __(917) 333-5555__
Message: __call about the
parent-teacher conference__

B

Date __11/9__ Time __1:30 P.M.__
To __Mr. Fong__

| **While You Were Out** |

From __Parker Sanchez__
Phone __(917) 333-5555__
Message: __call about the
parent-teacher conference__

C

GRAMMAR

Complete each conversation. What is the correct answer: A, B, or C?

9. **A:** Oleg is really good at speaking English.
   B: Yes, he speaks very _____.

   A. good
   B. clearly
   C. clear

10. **A:** I can't go to the kids' basketball game this Saturday.
    B: I can go, but _____ there until 1:00 P.M. I have to work on Saturday morning.

    A. I am not
    B. not
    C. I won't be

11. **A:** Laura is a good student.
    B: Yes. She does _____ in school.

    A. well
    B. good
    C. careful

12. **A:** Can you please help _____ with this homework?
    B: No, I'm sorry. I can't help you right now.

    A. I
    B. she
    C. us

13. **A:** My _____ name is Caroline.
    B: That's a beautiful name.

    A. daughter
    B. daughters'
    C. daughter's

14. **A:** Her parents _____ permission from the school to leave early next Friday.
    B: That's a good idea.

    A. gets
    B. will get
    C. get

15. **A:** Does Nelson have neat handwriting?
    B: No. He writes _____.

    A. bad
    B. poor
    C. poorly

16. A: Most of my _____ parents are very nice.

    B: That's great.

      A. student's

      B. students'

      C. students

17. A: Is the principal busy?

    B: No, you can see _____ now.

      A. him

      B. us

      C. them

18. A: We have a parent-teacher conference tomorrow night.

    B: OK. _____ home early.

      A. I am

      B. I'll be

      C. I was

19. A: Do Tina's children do well in school?

    B: Well, her _____ grades are good, but her daughter doesn't study very hard.

      A. son's

      B. son is

      C. sons

20. A: Melena _____ late for class tomorrow.

    B: OK, good.

      A. not be

      B. will not be

      C. will not

21. A: We can do _____!

    B: I know you can!

      A. you

      B. it

      C. they

22. A: I always make a lot of mistakes on my homework.

    B: That's because you do it _____. Be more careful when you work.

      A. quick

      B. careful

      C. quickly

23. A: Do you know Ms. Lancaster?

    B: Yes. I met _____ at the bake sale last weekend. She's nice.

      A. her

      B. she

      C. you

VOCABULARY

Read. What is the correct answer: A, B, C, or D?

①

②

③

④

24. My son gets good grades in math.

    A. ①

    B. ②

    C. ③

    D. ④

25. My uncle teaches music at the high school.

    A. ①

    B. ②

    C. ③

    D. ④

Read. What is the correct answer: A, B, C, or D?

Rafaela

Adu

26. Rafaela works hard in this class.

    A. music

    B. language arts

    C. art

    D. technology

27. Adu gets good grades in this class.

    A. world languages

    B. social studies/history

    C. community service

    D. physical education

LIFE SKILLS II

Read. What is the correct answer: A, B, C, or D?

> Dolores,
>
> Rose Chitembe (Linda's teacher) called
>
> about the bake sale. Please call her
>
> back. Her number is (213) 555-6129.
>
> Jake

28. Who called and left the message?

A. Dolores

B. Rose Chitembe

C. Linda

D. Jake

29. What is the message?

A. Linda's teacher wants Dolores to call her back.

B. Linda wants her mom to call her teacher.

C. Dolores wants Linda to call her.

D. Jake wants Linda's teacher to call him.

Read. What is the correct answer: A, B, C, or D?

Franklin High School
Enrollment Form

Student's Full Name: _____

❶ Gender: M__ F__ ❷ Date of Birth: _____ Phone: _____

Street Address: _____ City: _____ State: _____ Zip: _____

❸ Last School Attended: _____

Last School's Street Address: _____

City: _____ State: _____ Zip: _____

❹ Dates Enrolled: _____

Parents' Full Names: _____

Father's Employer: _____ Phone: _____

Mother's Employer: _____ Phone: _____

Local Emergency Contact: _____

Country of Birth: _____ Student's First Language: _____

Main Language Spoken at Home: _____

Other Languages Spoken at Home: _____

Did student study English as a second language? _____

Parent or Guardian Signature: _____

Date: _____

30. Where do you write the student's birthday?
    A. ①
    B. ②
    C. ③
    D. ④

31. Where do you write the name of the school the student went to before Franklin High School?
    A. ①
    B. ②
    C. ③
    D. ④

READING

Read. What is the correct answer: A, B, C, or D?

Bong-chol is in the fifth grade at Moreno Elementary School. He is a fast learner, and he studies hard. He's not very good at world languages, but he does very well in math. He always helps his friends with their math homework. There will be a big math test next week, and Bong-chol will help his friends study for it. He wants to be a math teacher when he grows up. He will be a good teacher!

32. How does Bong-chol do in school?

A. He learns quickly, but he doesn't study hard.

B. He is good at world languages.

C. He is good at math.

D. He doesn't help his friends with their homework.

33. What does Bong-chol want to do when he grows up?

A. He wants to help his friends study for the math test next week.

B. He wants to teach math.

C. He wants to teach world languages.

D. He wants to be in the fifth grade.

Unit 10 Test

LISTENING I

(Track 35) Look at the pictures and listen. What is the correct answer: A, B, or C?

1.

A   B   C

2.

A   B   C

🔘 LISTENING II

(Track 36) Listen to the question and three answers. What is the correct answer: A, B, or C?

3. A. I'll be back in a little while.

    B. Yes. I need some coffee.

    C. Sure, no problem.

4. A. Here you go.

    B. Could you get a gallon of apple cider?

    C. a side of French fries

(Track 37) Listen to the conversation. Then listen to the question and three answers. What is the correct answer: A, B, or C?

5. A. It is easier to prepare.

    B. It tastes good.

    C. It's better for you.

6. A. roast chicken and a side of coleslaw

    B. a fish sandwich and a side of coleslaw

    C. a fish sandwich and a side of mashed potatoes

GRAMMAR

Complete each conversation. What is the correct answer: A, B, or C?

7. **A:** _____ any cereal?
   B: Yes, there's a box on the counter.

   A. There's
   B. Are there
   C. Is there

8. **A:** Smoothy yogurt is _____ Kirklin yogurt.
   B: Yes, I think so too.

   A. delicious
   B. more delicious than
   C. better

9. **A:** We don't have _____ rice. Could you get a bag of rice at the grocery store?
   B: OK.

   A. much
   B. many
   C. some

10. **A:** I always make homemade meals for my kids.
    B: I do, too. They're _____ than fast food.

    A. healthy
    B. healthier
    C. health

11. **A:** _____ bunches of grapes do we need?
    B: One bunch is enough.

    A. How much
    B. How many
    C. Are there

12. **A:** Could you get some _____?
    B: OK. I'll get one dozen.

    A. egg
    B. eggs
    C. onion

13. **A:** Is there any butter?
    B: No, there _____.

    A. isn't any
    B. is some
    C. aren't any

14. **A:** Tomas needs oil to make dinner.
    B: _____ oil does he need?

    A. Is there any
    B. How much
    C. How many

15. **A:** Are there any oranges?
    B: Yes. There _____ oranges in the refrigerator.

    A. is some
    B. aren't any
    C. are some

16. **A:** _____ any potato chips?
    B: Yes, there are two bags on the counter.

    A. Is there
    B. There's
    C. Are there

17. **A:** Hamburgers are _____ chicken sandwiches.
    B: I know.

    A. more fattening than
    B. fattening than
    C. more fattening

18. **A:** Do we have vegetables for the salad?
    B: We have _____ carrots and tomatoes. We need some lettuce.

    A. much
    B. any
    C. a lot of

19. **A:** Do you eat _____ cheese?
    B: Yes. I eat it every day.

    A. much
    B. many
    C. a few

20. **A:** Those cookies don't have _____ nutrients.
    B: I know, but I love them!

    A. a little
    B. many
    C. some

21. **A:** My family eats a lot of cereal with fiber.
    B: Good. Cereal with fiber is _____ than cereal with no fiber.

    A. more nutritious
    B. healthy
    C. nutritious

VOCABULARY

Read. What is the correct answer: A, B, C, or D?

22. Could you get me a box of cereal at the store?
    A. ①
    B. ②
    C. ③
    D. ④

23. There's a jar of mayonnaise in the refrigerator.
    A. ①
    B. ②
    C. ③
    D. ④

Read. What is the correct answer: A, B, C, or D?

24. I need a half gallon of milk.
   A. ①
   B. ②
   C. ③
   D. ④

25. We need a little milk. Can you buy a pint at the supermarket?
   A. ①
   B. ②
   C. ③
   D. ④

LIFE SKILLS

Read. What is the correct answer: A, B, C, or D?

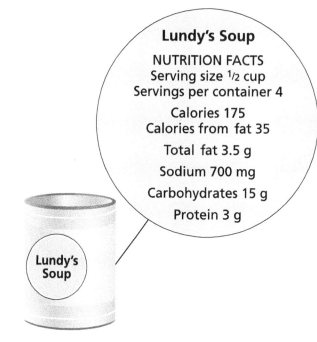

Choice Soup

NUTRITION FACTS
Serving size ½ cup
Servings per container 3

Calories 100
Calories from fat 15

Total fat 1.5 g

Sodium 900 mg

Carbohydrates 10 g

Protein 5 g

Choice Soup

Lundy's Soup

NUTRITION FACTS
Serving size ½ cup
Servings per container 4

Calories 175
Calories from fat 35

Total fat 3.5 g

Sodium 700 mg

Carbohydrates 15 g

Protein 3 g

Lundy's Soup

26. What does Choice Soup have?

   A. more fat than Lundy's Soup

   B. more calories than Lundy's Soup

   C. more carbohydrates than Lundy's Soup

   D. more sodium than Lundy's Soup

27. What does Lundy's Soup have?

   A. a bigger serving size than Choice Soup

   B. more calories from fat than Choice Soup

   C. more protein than Choice Soup

   D. more sodium than ChoiceSoup

28. How many servings per container does Lundy's Soup have?

   A. 4

   B. 35

   C. 3.5

   D. 700

29. How many calories does Choice Soup have?

   A. 900

   B. 10

   C. 100

   D. 3

Read. What is the correct answer: A, B, C, or D?

> **Protein** makes your body strong. Foods such as chicken, fish, and beans have a lot of protein.
>
> **Sodium** is another word for salt. Foods such as potato chips, canned soups, and olives have a lot of sodium.
>
> **Sugar** gives you quick energy. Candy, cookies, and soda have a lot of sugar.

30. Which food has a lot of sodium?

A. chicken

B. soda

C. potato chips

D. candy

31. Which food has a lot of protein?

A. beans

B. olives

C. cookies

D. canned soups

READING
Read. What is the correct answer: A, B, C, or D?

When Rong was younger, she ate a lot of fattening food. Now Rong eats nutritious food. She eats a lot of fish. It is healthier than hamburgers. She also eats more fruits and vegetables. They have a lot of fiber. Rong also eats fresh food because it is tastier than canned food. Rong always reads nutrition labels when she shops. She makes sure that the food she buys is good for her.

32. What kind of food does Rong eat now?

  A. fattening food

  B. healthy food

  C. canned food

  D. food with a lot of cholesterol and sodium in it

33. Why does Rong read nutrition labels on food?

  A. to check the price of the food

  B. to see what is in the food

  C. to find out how heavy the food is

  D. to find out how delicious the food is

Unit 11 Test

LISTENING I

(Track 38) **Look at the pictures and listen. What is the correct answer: A, B, or C?**

1.

A   **B**   **C**

2.

A   **B**   **C**

💿 LISTENING II

(Track 39) Listen to the question and three answers. What is the correct answer: A, B, or C?

3. A. I'm not sure.

   B. OK. They're in my glove compartment.

   C. You can get them.

4. A. A man is unconscious.

   B. This is Angelica Torres.

   C. Melvin's Deli at 420 Main Street.

(Track 40) Listen to the conversation. Then listen to the question and three answers. What is the correct answer: A, B, or C?

5. A. No one was hurt.

   B. There was a car accident.

   C. There was a construction accident.

6. A. A woman is unconscious.

   B. A woman fell.

   C. A woman burned herself.

GRAMMAR

Complete each conversation. What is the correct answer: A, B, or C?

7. **A:** What's the emergency?
   B: My husband _____!

   A. breathing
   B. is not breathing
   C. are not breathing

8. **A:** _____ or speed. It's dangerous.
   B: I know.

   A. Don't tailgate
   B. Tailgate
   C. Tailgating

9. **A:** There's an ambulance in front of Otto's house! What's _____?
   B: Otto's mom is unconscious!

   A. happening
   B. happens
   C. happen

10. **A:** _____ any injuries in the explosion.
    B: Oh, good.

    A. There wasn't
    B. There were
    C. There weren't

11. **A:** _____ your seat belt or read a map while driving.
    B: OK, officer.

    A. Don't take off
    B. Taking off
    C. Take off

12. **A:** Is Frank calling the police?
    B: No, _____.

    A. not calling
    B. isn't calling
    C. he's not

13. **A:** Is Boris driving Casimir to the emergency room?
    B: Yes, _____.

    A. he isn't
    B. he is
    C. is going

14. **A:** Was there a fire in your apartment yesterday?
    B: No, _____.

    A. there wasn't
    B. there was
    C. there weren't

15. **A:** It's raining. Turn on your headlights _____ carefully.
    B: OK, I will.

    A. and drive
    B. or drive
    C. drive

16. **A:** Don't use a cell phone _____ take off your seat belt while the car is moving.
    B: I won't.

    A. and
    B. or
    C. or don't

17. **A:** _____ customers in the store during the robbery?
    B: Yes, there were two men.

    A. Is there
    B. Was there
    C. Were there

18. **A:** A policeman is pulling us over!
    B: It's OK. Pull over to a safe spot _____ down your window.

    A. and roll
    B. or roll
    C. and don't

19. **A:** _____ a car accident last night.
    B: Was anybody hurt?

    A. There isn't
    B. There was
    C. There weren't

20. **A:** Is Bin _____ an allergic reaction?
    B: Yes, he is. Can you call 911?

    A. have
    B. has
    C. having

21. **A:** Where _____?
    B: They're going to the clinic.

    A. they are going
    B. are they going
    C. are going

VOCABULARY

Read. What is the correct answer: A, B, C, or D?

Kai   **Mei Ling**

Ted

22. What's happening to Kai?

A. He's unconscious.

B. He's choking.

C. He's bleeding.

D. He's burning himself.

23. What's wrong with Ted?

A. He's having a heart attack.

B. He burned himself.

C. He fell.

D. He's bleeding.

Read. What is the correct answer: A, B, C, or D?

Pilar

Anna

24. What's happening to Pilar?

    A. She's having trouble breathing.

    B. She's having a heart attack.

    C. She's falling.

    D. She's swallowing poison.

25. What happened to Anna?

    A. She had an allergic reaction.

    B. She was unconscious.

    C. She fell.

    D. She burned herself.

Future 2 Unit 11 Test **99**

LIFE SKILLS

Read. What is the correct answer: A, B, C, or D?

①

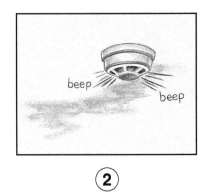

②

26. What is Picture ①?

    A. a fire extinguisher

    B. a smoke alarm

    C. a fire escape

    D. a fire hazard

27. What is Picture ②?

    A. a window exit

    B. a smoke alarm

    C. a fire extinguisher

    D. an escape plan

Read. What is the correct answer: A, B, C, or D?

IF THERE IS A FIRE...
- Leave your home immediately. Do not take anything with you.
- If you smell smoke, stay close to the floor.
- Use the stairs to leave the building. Don't use the elevator.
- Call 911 from outside the building.
- Wait outside the building until the fire is out.

28. When there is a fire, what's the first thing you should do?

A. Leave your home.

B. Use the elevator.

C. Call 911.

D. Wait until the fire is out.

29. What is dangerous to do in a fire?

A. Wait outside the building.

B. Use the stairs to leave the building.

C. Call 911 from outside your building.

D. Take things with you from your home.

30. What should you do if you smell smoke?

A. Run as fast as you can.

B. Stay close to the floor.

C. Lie down on the floor and don't move.

D. Climb on a chair or table.

READING

Read. What is the correct answer: A, B, C, or D?

There was a robbery at Glitter Jewelry Store yesterday. Two robbers ran into the store. They took a lot of jewelry. Then they ran away. Majid, the store manager, was not hurt. There were two customers in the store. One of the customers, an old woman, was very scared. She had trouble breathing. Then she fell on the floor and hurt her leg. Majid called 911. Some police and an ambulance came. There was a big crowd of people. The ambulance took the old woman to the hospital.

31. What happened at the jewelry store yesterday?

A. There was a fire.

B. There was a robbery.

C. There weren't any injuries.

D. There was a car accident.

32. Who was hurt?

A. Majid

B. two customers

C. the robbers

D. one customer

33. What happened after Majid called 911?

A. The robbers ran away.

B. Many ambulances came.

C. Some police and an ambulance came.

D. The ambulance took Majid to the hospital.

Unit 12 Test

LISTENING I

(Track 41) Look at the pictures and listen. What is the correct answer: A, B, or C?

1.

A

B

C

2.

A

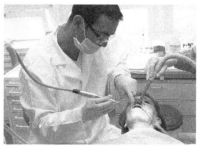

B

C

LISTENING II

(Track 42) **Listen to the question and three answers. What is the correct answer: A, B, or C?**

3. A. I'm glad I asked.

    B. What do you want to know?

    C. No, you aren't.

4. A. Sure. What is it?

    B. I'm on the schedule for Tuesday.

    C. I'll get back to you.

(Track 43) **Listen to the conversation. Then listen to the question and three answers. What is the correct answer: A, B, or C?**

5. A. go to the doctor

    B. take the man's shift for him

    C. take the day off

6. A. She wants to get another job.

    B. She wants to work in the evenings.

    C. She wants to work in the mornings.

GRAMMAR

Complete each conversation. What is the correct answer: A, B, or C?

7. **A:** Can we wear white shoes at work?
   B: No. We _____ wear black shoes.

   A. has to
   B. must
   C. have

8. **A:** Tanya started work late today.
   B: _____ did she start?

   A. Who
   B. Which days
   C. What time

9. **A:** Smoking is not allowed. You _____ smoke here.
   B: OK. I'll go outside.

   A. have to
   B. must
   C. must not

10. **A:** _____ take next week off?
    B: I think so.

    A. Could
    B. Can I
    C. I could

11. **A:** _____ your shift for you?
    B: Anh took my shift for me.

    A. Who took
    B. Who takes
    C. Who does

12. **A:** _____ about the schedule?
    B: She asked me.

    A. Who does
    B. Who did she
    C. Who did she ask

13. **A:** What can front desk employees wear?
    B: They _____ blue uniforms.

    A. have to
    B. must
    C. have to wear

14. A: Could I go home at 3:00?

    B: Yes, _____.

      A. you go

      B. you can

      C. could

15. A: I have a new work schedule.

    B: Oh, really? _____ do you work now?

      A. Where

      B. Which days

      C. Who

16. A: Carlos can't come in tomorrow.

    B: He _____ come in! There's a very important meeting. I'll talk to him.

      A. must not

      B. has to

      C. have to

17. A: _____ a question?

    B: Sure. What is it?

      A. Can I ask

      B. Can I

      C. Could I

18. A: _____ a break at 10:30 A.M.?

    B: Candice takes her break at 10:30.

      A. What time does she

      B. When does she take

      C. Who takes

19. A: _____ work the second shift next week?

    B: Let me check the schedule. I'll get back to you.

      A. I can

      B. I could

      C. Could I

20. A: You _____ forget to clock in and out.

    B: OK. I understand.

      A. must

      B. must not

      C. have to

21. A: Which days do you want to work next week, Susana?

    B: _____ on Tuesday and Thursday?

      A. Can I

      B. Could I

      C. Can I work

VOCABULARY

Read. What is the correct answer: A, B, C, or D?

(1)

(2)

(3)

(4)

22. Warehouse workers have to store equipment.

A. ①

B. ②

C. ③

D. ④

23. Many employees have to clock in and out every day.

A. ①

B. ②

C. ③

D. ④

24. All employees must wear safety gear.

A. ①

B. ②

C. ③

D. ④

Read. What is the correct answer: A, B, C, or D?

Ernesto

25. What does Ernesto have to do at work?

   A. He has to wear latex gloves.

   B. He has to wear safety gear.

   C. He has to wear a white uniform.

   D. He has to wear a black uniform.

LIFE SKILLS

Read. What is the correct answer: A, B, C, or D?

Michael Chen			Pay Date 6/20	Pay Period 6/2–6/15	Rate of Pay $10.00
Description	**Hours**	**Earnings**	**Deductions**		**Amount**
Regular	80	$800.00	Federal Tax		$107.05
Overtime	10	$150.00	State Tax		$24.70
			FICA ⌐Social Security		$30.40
			└Medicare		$16.77
Total Gross Pay		$950.00	**Total Deductions**	$178.92	**Net Pay** $771.08

26. How much money does Michael get per hour?
    A. $10.00
    B. $800.00
    C. $150.00
    D. $950.00

27. How many total hours did Michael work this week?
    A. 80
    B. 10
    C. 90
    D. 771

28. How much money was taken out in state tax?
    A. $107.05
    B. $30.40
    C. $24.70
    D. $16.77

29. How much money did Michael get after deductions?
    A. $178.92
    B. $771.08
    C. $800.00
    D. $950.00

Read. What is the correct answer: A, B, C, or D?

VACATION REQUEST FORM

Employee _____ ❶ Date of Hire _____

Department _____

❷ Number of Vacation Days Requested _____

❸ Dates Requested _____

Employee Signature _____ ❹ Date _____

Supervisor Signature _____ Date _____

30. Where do you write the day that you started work?

A. ①

B. ②

C. ③

D. ④

31. Where do you write the dates that you want to go on vacation?

A. ①

B. ②

C. ③

D. ④

READING

Read. What is the correct answer: A, B, C, or D?

Raymundo is a supervisor at the Metro Bus Company. He has to train all the new employees. All the employees have to clock in and out every day. They must also call Raymundo if they are going to be late to work. They are not allowed to make personal calls at work. Raymundo also makes up the schedule. Sometimes employees can't work their shifts. Then Raymundo has to find other workers to cover the shifts. Raymundo is a good supervisor, and his workers like him a lot.

32. What are Raymundo's job responsibilities?

    A. He trains new employees.

    B. He calls his employees if he is going to be late to work.

    C. He makes personal calls at work.

    D. He covers shifts when his employees can't work.

33. What must employees at the Metro Bus Company do?

    A. They must clock in and out every day.

    B. They must make up the schedule.

    C. They must call Raymundo if they are going to be on time.

    D. They must supervise the new employees.

Future 2
Unit Test Answer Sheet

① _____

   Last Name   First Name   Middle

② _____

   Teacher's Name

TEST

1. (A) (B) (C) (D)
2. (A) (B) (C) (D)
3. (A) (B) (C) (D)
4. (A) (B) (C) (D)
5. (A) (B) (C) (D)
6. (A) (B) (C) (D)
7. (A) (B) (C) (D)
8. (A) (B) (C) (D)
9. (A) (B) (C) (D)
10. (A) (B) (C) (D)
11. (A) (B) (C) (D)
12. (A) (B) (C) (D)
13. (A) (B) (C) (D)
14. (A) (B) (C) (D)
15. (A) (B) (C) (D)
16. (A) (B) (C) (D)
17. (A) (B) (C) (D)
18. (A) (B) (C) (D)
19. (A) (B) (C) (D)
20. (A) (B) (C) (D)
21. (A) (B) (C) (D)
22. (A) (B) (C) (D)
23. (A) (B) (C) (D)
24. (A) (B) (C) (D)
25. (A) (B) (C) (D)
26. (A) (B) (C) (D)
27. (A) (B) (C) (D)
28. (A) (B) (C) (D)
29. (A) (B) (C) (D)
30. (A) (B) (C) (D)
31. (A) (B) (C) (D)
32. (A) (B) (C) (D)
33. (A) (B) (C) (D)

Directions for marking answers

- Use a No. 2 pencil. Do NOT use ink.
- Make dark marks and bubble in your answers completely.
- If you change an answer, erase your first mark completely.

Right
(A) (B) (C) (D)

Wrong
(A) (B) (C) (D)
(A) (B) (C) (D)

③ STUDENT IDENTIFICATION

```
0 0 0   0 0   0 0 0 0
1 1 1   1 1   1 1 1 1
2 2 2   2 2   2 2 2 2
3 3 3   3 3   3 3 3 3
4 4 4   4 4   4 4 4 4
5 5 5   5 5   5 5 5 5
6 6 6   6 6   6 6 6 6
7 7 7   7 7   7 7 7 7
8 8 8   8 8   8 8 8 8
9 9 9   9 9   9 9 9 9
```

Is this your Social Security number?
Yes ☐   No ☐

④ TEST DATE

MM	D	D	Y	Y
Jan ☐	0	0	200	9
Feb ☐	1	1	201	0
Mar ☐	2	2	201	1
Apr ☐	3	3	201	2
May ☐		4	201	3
Jun ☐		5	201	4
Jul ☐		6	201	5
Aug ☐		7	201	6
Sep ☐		8	201	7
Oct ☐		9	201	8
Nov ☐				
Dec ☐				

⑤ CLASS NUMBER

```
0 0 0 0 0 0 0 0
1 1 1 1 1 1 1 1
2 2 2 2 2 2 2 2
3 3 3 3 3 3 3 3
4 4 4 4 4 4 4 4
5 5 5 5 5 5 5 5
6 6 6 6 6 6 6 6
7 7 7 7 7 7 7 7
8 8 8 8 8 8 8 8
9 9 9 9 9 9 9 9
```

⑥ RAW SCORE

```
0 0
1 1
2 2
3 3
4 4
5 5
6 6
7 7
8 8
9 9
```

Unit 1 Test Answer Key

ANSWERS	LESSON/PAGE	OBJECTIVE
1 Ⓐ Ⓑ Ⓒ Ⓓ	2, p. 8	Describe the way people look
2 Ⓐ Ⓑ Ⓒ Ⓓ	2, p. 8	Describe the way people look
3 Ⓐ Ⓑ Ⓒ Ⓓ	8, p. 20	Get to know someone
4 Ⓐ Ⓑ Ⓒ Ⓓ	8, p. 20	Get to know someone
5 Ⓐ Ⓑ Ⓒ Ⓓ	2, p. 8	Talk about what you are doing
6 Ⓐ Ⓑ Ⓒ Ⓓ	5, p. 14	Describe personalities
7 Ⓐ Ⓑ Ⓒ Ⓓ	3, p. 10	Simple present: *Have* + object
8 Ⓐ Ⓑ Ⓒ Ⓓ	6, p. 16	*Be:* Compound sentences with *and/but*
9 Ⓐ Ⓑ Ⓒ Ⓓ	6, p. 17	*Be:* Additions with *and…/too/ and…not, either*
10 Ⓐ Ⓑ Ⓒ Ⓓ	6, p. 16	*Be:* Compound sentences with *and/but*
11 Ⓐ Ⓑ Ⓒ Ⓓ	6, p. 17	*Be:* Additions with *and…/too/ and…not, either*
12 Ⓐ Ⓑ Ⓒ Ⓓ	6, p. 17	*Be:* Additions with *and…/too/ and…not, either*
13 Ⓐ Ⓑ Ⓒ Ⓓ	9, p. 22	Simple present tense of *be: Yes/No* and information questions
14 Ⓐ Ⓑ Ⓒ Ⓓ	9, p. 22	Simple present tense of *be: Yes/No* and information questions
15 Ⓐ Ⓑ Ⓒ Ⓓ	6, p. 17	*Be:* Additions with *and…/too/ and…not, either*
16 Ⓐ Ⓑ Ⓒ Ⓓ	9, p. 22	Simple present tense of *be: Yes/No* and information questions
17 Ⓐ Ⓑ Ⓒ Ⓓ	9, p. 22	Simple present tense of *be: Yes/No* and information questions
18 Ⓐ Ⓑ Ⓒ Ⓓ	3, p. 10	Simple present: *Be* + adjective
19 Ⓐ Ⓑ Ⓒ Ⓓ	6, p. 16	*Be:* Compound sentences with *and/but*
20 Ⓐ Ⓑ Ⓒ Ⓓ	6, p. 16	*Be:* Compound sentences with *and/but*
21 Ⓐ Ⓑ Ⓒ Ⓓ	3, p. 10	Simple present: *Have* + object
22 Ⓐ Ⓑ Ⓒ Ⓓ	1, p. 6	Make physical descriptions
23 Ⓐ Ⓑ Ⓒ Ⓓ	1, p. 6	Make physical descriptions
24 Ⓐ Ⓑ Ⓒ Ⓓ	1, p. 6	Make physical descriptions
25 Ⓐ Ⓑ Ⓒ Ⓓ	1, p. 6	Make physical descriptions
26 Ⓐ Ⓑ Ⓒ Ⓓ	4, p. 12	Complete an application
27 Ⓐ Ⓑ Ⓒ Ⓓ	4, p. 12	Complete an application
28 Ⓐ Ⓑ Ⓒ Ⓓ	4, p. 12	Complete an application
29 Ⓐ Ⓑ Ⓒ Ⓓ	4, p. 12	Complete an application
30 Ⓐ Ⓑ Ⓒ Ⓓ	4, p. 12	Complete an application
31 Ⓐ Ⓑ Ⓒ Ⓓ	4, p. 12	Complete an application
32 Ⓐ Ⓑ Ⓒ Ⓓ		Read for details
33 Ⓐ Ⓑ Ⓒ Ⓓ		Read for details

Please see reverse for test audio script.

Unit 1 Test Audio Script

Listening I
(Track 5) Page 1. Look at the pictures and listen.
What is the correct answer: A, B, or C?

1. Veronica's sister has short, curly hair.
2. Sandy is pretty.

Listening II
(Track 6) Page 2. Listen to the question and three answers.
What is the correct answer: A, B, or C?

3. What's Argentina like?
   A. Where are you from?
   B. Oh, that's nice.
   C. It's a very beautiful country.

4. Are you students?
   A. No, we're from Hawaii.
   B. Yes, we're in Mr. Carter's English class.
   C. Yes, it's a beautiful country.

(Track 7) Page 2. Listen to the conversation. Then listen to the question and three answers.
What is the correct answer: A, B, or C?

5. **M:** Are you coming to my party?
   F: No, I'm working tonight.

   What is the woman doing tonight?
   A. She is working.
   B. She is coming to the party.
   C. She is having a party.

6. **F1:** What's Walter like?
   F2: He's attractive, but quiet.

   What's the man like?
   A. He's talkative.
   B. He's tall and thin.
   C. He's quiet and attractive.

Unit 2 Test Answer Key

	ANSWERS	LESSON/PAGE	OBJECTIVE
1	Ⓐ Ⓑ **Ⓒ** Ⓓ	2, p. 28	Talk about life and family
2	Ⓐ Ⓑ **Ⓒ** Ⓓ	8, p. 40	Ask about family members
3	Ⓐ **Ⓑ** Ⓒ Ⓓ	8, p. 40	Ask about family members
4	Ⓐ Ⓑ **Ⓒ** Ⓓ	2, p. 28	Talk about life and family
5	Ⓐ **Ⓑ** Ⓒ Ⓓ	5, p. 34	Talk about what people have in common
6	**Ⓐ** Ⓑ Ⓒ Ⓓ	5, p. 34	Talk about what people have in common
7	Ⓐ Ⓑ **Ⓒ** Ⓓ	3, p. 30	Simple present affirmative and negative: *Have/live/work*
8	Ⓐ **Ⓑ** Ⓒ Ⓓ	6, p. 36	Simple present: Additions with *and…, too/and…not, either*
9	**Ⓐ** Ⓑ Ⓒ Ⓓ	3, p. 30	Simple present affirmative and negative: *Have/live/work*
10	Ⓐ Ⓑ **Ⓒ** Ⓓ	6, p. 36	Simple present: Additions with *and…, too/and…not, either*
11	Ⓐ **Ⓑ** Ⓒ Ⓓ	9, p. 42	Simple present: Information questions and answers
12	Ⓐ Ⓑ **Ⓒ** Ⓓ	9, p. 42	Simple present: *Yes/no* questions and answers
13	**Ⓐ** Ⓑ Ⓒ Ⓓ	3, p. 30	Simple present affirmative and negative: *Have/live/work*
14	**Ⓐ** Ⓑ Ⓒ Ⓓ	6, p. 36	Simple present: Additions with *and…, too/and…not, either*
15	**Ⓐ** Ⓑ Ⓒ Ⓓ	9, p. 42	Simple present: *Yes/no* questions and answers
16	Ⓐ **Ⓑ** Ⓒ Ⓓ	3, p. 30	Simple present affirmative and negative: *Have/live/work*
17	Ⓐ **Ⓑ** Ⓒ Ⓓ	6, p. 36	Simple present: Additions with *and…, too/and…not, either*
18	Ⓐ Ⓑ **Ⓒ** Ⓓ	3, p. 30	Simple present affirmative and negative: *Have/live/work*
19	Ⓐ Ⓑ **Ⓒ** Ⓓ	9, p. 42	Simple present: *Yes/no* questions and answers
20	Ⓐ **Ⓑ** Ⓒ Ⓓ	6, p. 36	Simple present: Additions with *and…, too/and…not, either*
21	Ⓐ **Ⓑ** Ⓒ Ⓓ	9, p. 42	Simple present: Information questions and answers
22	Ⓐ Ⓑ **Ⓒ** Ⓓ	1, p. 26	Identify family members
23	**Ⓐ** Ⓑ Ⓒ Ⓓ	1, p. 26	Identify family members
24	**Ⓐ** Ⓑ Ⓒ Ⓓ	1, p. 26	Identify family members
25	**Ⓐ** Ⓑ Ⓒ Ⓓ	1, p. 26	Identify family members
26	Ⓐ Ⓑ **Ⓒ** Ⓓ	7, p. 38	Ask about sending mail
27	Ⓐ **Ⓑ** Ⓒ Ⓓ	7, p. 38	Ask about sending mail
28	**Ⓐ** Ⓑ Ⓒ Ⓓ	7, p. 38	Ask about sending mail
29	Ⓐ Ⓑ Ⓒ **Ⓓ**	7, p. 38	Ask about sending mail
30	Ⓐ Ⓑ **Ⓒ** Ⓓ	LSW, p. 257	Complete a post office customs form
31	**Ⓐ** Ⓑ Ⓒ Ⓓ	LSW, p. 257	Complete a post office customs form
32	Ⓐ Ⓑ **Ⓒ** Ⓓ		Read for details
33	Ⓐ Ⓑ Ⓒ **Ⓓ**		Read for details

Please see reverse for test audio script.

Unit 2 Test Audio Script

Listening I
(Track 8) Page 10. Look at the pictures and listen.
What is the correct answer: A, B, or C?

1. Mia has a very big family.
2. Carolina emails her family once a week.

Listening II
(Track 9) Page 11. Listen to the question and three answers.
What is the correct answer: A, B, or C?

3. How often do you keep in touch with your friends?
   A. Yes, I call them.
   B. I call them a few times a month.
   C. I have a lot of friends.

4. Do your brothers live here?
   A. Tell me about your family.
   B. I don't have a very big family.
   C. No, they don't. They live in China.

(Track 10) Page 11. Listen to the conversation. Then listen to the question and three answers.
What is the correct answer: A, B, or C?

5. **M:** Do you have a lot in common with your brother?
   F: Yes. We both have three kids.

   What does the woman's brother have?
   A. six kids
   B. three kids
   C. no kids

6. **M:** Jean, is this your daughter? You two look alike.
   F: No, that's my niece, Patty.

   Who is Patty?
   A. the woman's niece
   B. the woman's daughter
   C. the man's niece

Unit 3 Test Answer Key

	ANSWERS	LESSON/PAGE	OBJECTIVE
1	Ⓐ Ⓑ Ⓒ Ⓓ	2, p. 48	Describe wants and needs
2	Ⓐ Ⓑ Ⓒ Ⓓ	5, p. 54	Talk about shopping plans
3	Ⓐ Ⓑ Ⓒ Ⓓ	8, p. 60	Describe problems with purchases
4	Ⓐ Ⓑ Ⓒ Ⓓ	8, p. 60	Describe problems with purchases
5	Ⓐ Ⓑ Ⓒ Ⓓ	5, p. 54	Talk about shopping plans
6	Ⓐ Ⓑ Ⓒ Ⓓ	2, p. 48	Describe wants and needs
7	Ⓐ Ⓑ Ⓒ Ⓓ	4, p. 53	Pay for things
8	Ⓐ Ⓑ Ⓒ Ⓓ	3, p. 50	Simple present: *Want/need* + infinitive
9	Ⓐ Ⓑ Ⓒ Ⓓ	3, p. 50	Simple present: *Want/need* + infinitive
10	Ⓐ Ⓑ Ⓒ Ⓓ	3, p. 50	Simple present: *Want/need* + infinitive
11	Ⓐ Ⓑ Ⓒ Ⓓ	9, p. 62	Adverbs of degree: *Very/too*
12	Ⓐ Ⓑ Ⓒ Ⓓ	6, p. 56	*Be going to*
13	Ⓐ Ⓑ Ⓒ Ⓓ	6, p. 56	*Be going to*
14	Ⓐ Ⓑ Ⓒ Ⓓ	6, p. 56	*Be going to*
15	Ⓐ Ⓑ Ⓒ Ⓓ	6, p. 56	*Be going to*
16	Ⓐ Ⓑ Ⓒ Ⓓ	9, p. 62	Adverbs of degree: *Very/too*
17	Ⓐ Ⓑ Ⓒ Ⓓ	6, p. 56	*Be going to*
18	Ⓐ Ⓑ Ⓒ Ⓓ	9, p. 62	Adverbs of degree: *Very/too*
19	Ⓐ Ⓑ Ⓒ Ⓓ	3, p. 50	Simple present: *Want/need* + infinitive
20	Ⓐ Ⓑ Ⓒ Ⓓ	9, p. 62	Adverbs of degree: *Very/too*
21	Ⓐ Ⓑ Ⓒ Ⓓ	3, p. 50	Simple present: *Want/need* + infinitive
22	Ⓐ Ⓑ Ⓒ Ⓓ	9, p. 62	Adverbs of degree: *Very/too*
23	Ⓐ Ⓑ Ⓒ Ⓓ	1, p. 46	Identify clothes and materials
24	Ⓐ Ⓑ Ⓒ Ⓓ	1, p. 46	Identify clothes and materials
25	Ⓐ Ⓑ Ⓒ Ⓓ	1, p. 46	Identify clothes and materials
26	Ⓐ Ⓑ Ⓒ Ⓓ	1, p. 46	Identify clothes and materials
27	Ⓐ Ⓑ Ⓒ Ⓓ	4, p. 52	Pay for things
28	Ⓐ Ⓑ Ⓒ Ⓓ	4, p. 52	Pay for things
29	Ⓐ Ⓑ Ⓒ Ⓓ	4, p. 52	Pay for things
30	Ⓐ Ⓑ Ⓒ Ⓓ	LSW, p. 258	Interpret a personal check
31	Ⓐ Ⓑ Ⓒ Ⓓ	LSW, p. 258	Interpret a personal check
32	Ⓐ Ⓑ Ⓒ Ⓓ		Read for details
33	Ⓐ Ⓑ Ⓒ Ⓓ		Read for details

Please see reverse for test audio script.

Unit 3 Test Audio Script

Listening I
(Track 11) Page 19. Look at the pictures and listen.
What is the correct answer: A, B, or C?

1. I need to buy a new jacket for my friend.
2. He's going to stop at the bank.

Listening II
(Track 12) Page 20. Listen to the question and three answers.
What is the correct answer: A, B, or C?

3. Could you return these gloves for me?
   A. Where do you like to shop?
   B. I need to go to the ATM.
   C. Sure. I'm going to the mall tomorrow.

4. What's wrong with your jeans?
   A. I need new gloves.
   B. The zipper is broken.
   C. I'm going to stop at the supermarket.

(Track 13) Page 20. Listen to the conversation. Then listen to the question and three answers.
What is the correct answer: A, B, or C?

5. **M:** What are Julie's plans for the weekend?
   F: She needs to go to the laundromat and stop at the bank.

   What's Julie going to do?
   A. She's going to relax.
   B. She's going to stop at the pharmacy.
   C. She's going to the bank and the laundromat.

6. **M:** It's so hot this month!
   F: I know. It feels like summer. I need to buy a swimsuit.

   What's the weather like?
   A. cold
   B. hot
   C. cool

Life Skills I
(Track 14) Page 21. Look at the pictures and listen.
What is the correct answer: A, B, or C?

7. **M:** Excuse me. I think there's a mistake. The ad says all sunglasses are 40 percent off.
      But my receipt says 20 percent off.
   F: Oh, I'm sorry. I'll take care of that.

Unit 4 Test Answer Key

	ANSWERS	LESSON/PAGE	OBJECTIVE
1	(A) (B) (C) (D)	2, p. 68	Talk about weekend activities
2	(A) (B) (C) (D)	5, p. 74	Communicating likes and dislikes
3	(A) (B) (C) (D)	2, p. 68	Talk about weekend activities
4	(A) (B) (C) (D)	8, p. 80	Accept or decline an invitation
5	(A) (B) (C) (D)	8, p. 80	Accept or decline an invitation
6	(A) (B) (C) (D)	2, p. 68	Talk about weekend activities
7	(A) (B) (C) (D)	3, p. 71	Questions with *How often*/frequency time expressions
8	(A) (B) (C) (D)	6, p. 76	Simple present: *Like/love/hate* + infinitive
9	(A) (B) (C) (D)	9, p. 82	Modal: *Have to*
10	(A) (B) (C) (D)	3, p. 70	Adverbs of frequency
11	(A) (B) (C) (D)	3, p. 70	Adverbs of frequency
12	(A) (B) (C) (D)	9, p. 82	Modal: *Have to*
13	(A) (B) (C) (D)	6, p. 76	Simple present: *Like/love/hate* + infinitive
14	(A) (B) (C) (D)	3, p. 70	Adverbs of frequency
15	(A) (B) (C) (D)	3, p. 70	Adverbs of frequency
16	(A) (B) (C) (D)	6, p. 76	Simple present: *Like/love/hate* + infinitive
17	(A) (B) (C) (D)	6, p. 76	Simple present: *Like/love/hate* + infinitive
18	(A) (B) (C) (D)	3, p. 71	Questions with *How often*/frequency time expressions
19	(A) (B) (C) (D)	3, p. 70	Adverbs of frequency
20	(A) (B) (C) (D)	9, p. 82	Modal: *Have to*
21	(A) (B) (C) (D)	9, p. 82	Modal: *Have to*
22	(A) (B) (C) (D)	1, p. 66	Identify free-time activities
23	(A) (B) (C) (D)	1, p. 66	Identify free-time activities
24	(A) (B) (C) (D)	1, p. 66	Identify free-time activities
25	(A) (B) (C) (D)	1, p. 66	Identify free-time activities
26	(A) (B) (C) (D)	4, p. 72	Plan activities using a calendar
27	(A) (B) (C) (D)	4, p. 72	Plan activities using a calendar
28	(A) (B) (C) (D)	4, p. 72	Plan activities using a calendar
29	(A) (B) (C) (D)	4, p. 72	Plan activities using a calendar
30	(A) (B) (C) (D)	4, p. 72	Plan activities using a calendar
31	(A) (B) (C) (D)		Read for details
32	(A) (B) (C) (D)		Read for details
33	(A) (B) (C) (D)		Read for details

Please see reverse for test audio script.

Unit 4 Test Audio Script

Listening I
(Track 15) Page 29. Look at the pictures and listen.
What is the correct answer: A, B, or C?

1. He has a guitar lesson every Wednesday.
2. You really hate to exercise.

Listening II
(Track 16) Page 30. Listen to the question and three answers.
What is the correct answer: A, B, or C?

3. What are your friends doing this weekend?
   A. Sounds like fun.
   B. What about you?
   C. They're going for a bike ride.

4. Do you want to take a walk?
   A. Sorry, I can't.
   B. I really hate to get up early.
   C. Really?

(Track 17) Page 30. Listen to the conversation. Then listen to the question and three answers.
What is the correct answer: A, B, or C?

5. **M:** Do you want to go dancing?
   F: Sorry, I can't. I really don't feel well.

   What's the matter?
   A. The woman has to work.
   B. The woman doesn't feel well.
   C. The woman has other plans.

6. **M:** I'm going to a karate class with my family tomorrow.
   F: Really? That sounds like fun!

   What's the man doing tomorrow?
   A. He's going to a computer class.
   B. He's going out to eat with his family.
   C. He's going to a karate class.

Unit 5 Test Answer Key

	ANSWERS	LESSON/PAGE	OBJECTIVE
1	(A) (B) **C** (D)	2, p. 88	Describe problems in a home
2	(A) **B** (C) (D)	2, p. 88	Describe problems in a home
3	(A) (B) **C** (D)	2, p. 88	Describe problems in a home
4	(A) **B** (C) (D)	5, p. 94	Ask about an apartment
5	**A** (B) (C) (D)	5, p. 94	Ask about an apartment
6	(A) **B** (C) (D)	8, p. 100	Get directions
7	(A) (B) **C** (D)	3, p. 90	Present continuous
8	**A** (B) (C) (D)	3, p. 90	Present continuous
9	(A) **B** (C) (D)	3, p. 90	Present continuous
10	(A) (B) **C** (D)	6, p. 96	*There is/There are*
11	**A** (B) (C) (D)	6, p. 96	*There is/There are*
12	(A) **B** (C) (D)	6, p. 96	*There is/There are*
13	(A) (B) **C** (D)	6, p. 96	*There is/There are*
14	**A** (B) (C) (D)	3, p. 90	Present continuous
15	**A** (B) (C) (D)	6, p. 96	*There is/There are*
16	(A) (B) **C** (D)	6, p. 96	*There is/There are*
17	(A) **B** (C) (D)	3, p. 90	Present continuous
18	(A) **B** (C) (D)	3, p. 90	Present continuous
19	(A) (B) **C** (D)	6, p. 96	Present continuous
20	**A** (B) (C) (D)	6, p. 96	*There is/There are*
21	(A) (B) **C** (D)	3, p. 90	*There is/There are*
22	(A) **B** (C) (D)	1, p. 86	Identify household problems
23	(A) (B) (C) **D**	1, p. 86	Identify household problems
24	(A) **B** (C) (D)	1, p. 86	Identify household problems
25	(A) (B) (C) **D**	1, p. 86	Identify household problems
26	(A) **B** (C) (D)	4, p. 92	Read apartment ads
27	(A) (B) **C** (D)	4, p. 92	Read apartment ads
28	(A) (B) **C** (D)	4, p. 92	Read apartment ads
29	(A) **B** (C) (D)	4, p. 92	Read apartment ads
30	(A) (B) **C** (D)	4, p. 92	Read apartment ads
31	(A) (B) (C) **D**	4, p. 92	Read apartment ads
32	(A) (B) **C** (D)		Read for details
33	(A) (B) **C** (D)		Read for details

Please see reverse for test audio script.

Unit 5 Test Audio Script

Listening I
(Track 18) Page 38. Look at the pictures and listen.
What is the correct answer: A, B, or C?

1. You should call the plumber.
2. My sink is clogged.

Listening II
(Track 19) Page 39. Listen to the question and three answers.
What is the correct answer: A, B, or C?

3. The bathroom light isn't working.
   A. Sure. No problem.
   B. Is there a park nearby?
   C. You should call the building manager.

4. Can you tell me about the apartment?
   A. Yes, there is.
   B. Sure. It has three bedrooms.
   C. Oh, good.

(Track 20) Page 39. Listen to the conversation. Then listen to the question and three answers.
What is the correct answer: A, B, or C?

5. **M:** Is there a parking lot near the apartment?
   F: No, there isn't. But there's free parking on the street.

   What's the problem with the apartment?
   A. There's no parking lot.
   B. There's no free parking on the street.
   C. There's no parking lot, and there isn't any free parking on the street.

6. **F:** Can you give me directions to the hospital?.
   M: Yes. Go straight on Second Street. It's on the right near the gas station.

   Where is the hospital?
   A. It's on First Street.
   B. It's on Second Street near the gas station.
   C. It's on the right near the pharmacy.

Unit 6 Test Answer Key

	ANSWERS	LESSON/PAGE	OBJECTIVE
1	Ⓐ Ⓑ © D	8, p. 120	Talk about something that happened
2	Ⓐ B C D	5, p. 114	Talk about milestones
3	A B © D	2, p. 108	Talk about past activities
4	A B © D	5, p. 114	Talk about milestones
5	Ⓐ B C D	8, p. 120	Talk about something that happened
6	A B © D	2, p. 108	Talk about past activities
7	A Ⓑ C D	4, p. 112	Recognize U.S. holidays
8	A B © D	4, p. 112	Recognize U.S. holidays
9	A B © D	6, p. 117	Simple past: *Yes/No* questions
10	A Ⓑ C D	6, p. 116	Simple past: Irregular verbs
11	Ⓐ B C D	6, p. 116	Simple past: Irregular verbs
12	A Ⓑ C D	3, p. 110	Simple past: Regular verbs
13	A B © D	6, p. 117	Simple past: *Yes/No* questions
14	A Ⓑ C D	9, p. 122	Simple past: Information questions
15	A B © D	6, p. 117	Simple past: *Yes/No* questions
16	Ⓐ B C D	3, p. 110	Simple past: Regular verbs
17	Ⓐ B C D	6, p. 116	Simple past: Irregular verbs
18	A B © D	9, p. 122	Simple past: Information questions
19	A Ⓑ C D	9, p. 122	Simple past: Information questions
20	A B © D	6, p. 116	Simple past: Irregular verbs
21	A Ⓑ C D	6, p. 117	Simple past: *Yes/No* questions
22	A Ⓑ C D	3, p. 110	Simple past: Regular verbs
23	Ⓐ B C D	3, p. 110	Simple past: Regular verbs
24	A B © D	1, p. 106	Identify events with family and friends
25	A Ⓑ C D	1, p. 106	Identify events with family and friends
26	A Ⓑ C D	1, p. 106	Identify events with family and friends
27	A B © D	1, p. 106	Identify events with family and friends
28	A B © D	4, p. 112	Recognize U.S. holidays
29	Ⓐ B C D	4, p. 112	Recognize U.S. holidays
30	A B © D	LSW, p. 261	Interpret an absence note to a teacher
31	Ⓐ B C D	LSW, p. 261	Interpret an absence note to a teacher
32	A B © D		Read for details
33	A B C Ⓓ		Read for details

Please see reverse for test audio script.

Unit 6 Test Audio Script

Listening I
(Track 21) Page 47. Look at the pictures and listen.
What is the correct answer: A, B, or C?

1. Hong got stuck in traffic.
2. I was born in a big city in Guatemala.

Listening II
(Track 22) Page 48. Listen to the question and three answers.
What is the correct answer: A, B, or C?

3. How was your weekend?
   A. Sounds great!
   B. It was really nice, thanks.
   C. How was the family reunion?

4. Did you study English in Korea?
   A. I always wanted to be an actor.
   B. I got married five years ago.
   C. Yes, I did, but I didn't practice speaking a lot.

(Track 23) Page 48. Listen to the conversation. Then listen to the question and three answers.
What is the correct answer: A, B, or C?

5. **M:** You look stressed out!
   F: Well, I had car trouble and was late to work!

   What happened to the woman?
   A. She was late to work.
   B. She took the wrong train.
   C. She overslept.

6. **F:** How was your weekend?
   M: It was fun. I played games with my aunts and uncles.

   What did the man do?
   A. He watched old movies with his aunts and uncles.
   B. He danced all night.
   C. He played games.

Life Skills I
(Track 24) Page 49. Look at the pictures and listen.
What is the correct answer: A, B, or C?

7. **M:** This is the first barbecue of the year!
   F: I can't believe that summer is almost here!

8. **M:** Mmm. The turkey smells so good!
   F: Yes. I'm happy that the whole family is coming to eat it!

Unit 7 Test Answer Key

ANSWERS	LESSON/PAGE	OBJECTIVE
1 Ⓐ Ⓑ Ⓒ Ⓓ (B)	2, p. 128	Talk about a health problem
2 Ⓐ Ⓑ Ⓒ Ⓓ (A)	5, p. 134	Talk about an injury
3 Ⓐ Ⓑ Ⓒ Ⓓ (C)	2, p. 128	Make a doctor's appointment
4 Ⓐ Ⓑ Ⓒ Ⓓ (A)	2, p. 128	Talk about a health problem
5 Ⓐ Ⓑ Ⓒ Ⓓ (C)	8, p. 140	Call in when you have to miss work
6 Ⓐ Ⓑ Ⓒ Ⓓ (B)	5, p. 134	Talk about an injury
7 Ⓐ Ⓑ Ⓒ Ⓓ (C)	6, p. 136	Simple past: Irregular verbs
8 Ⓐ Ⓑ Ⓒ Ⓓ (B)	3, p. 130	Prepositions of time
9 Ⓐ Ⓑ Ⓒ Ⓓ (A)	3, p. 130	Prepositions of time
10 Ⓐ Ⓑ Ⓒ Ⓓ (C)	6, p. 136	Simple past: Irregular verbs
11 Ⓐ Ⓑ Ⓒ Ⓓ (A)	3, p. 130	Prepositions of time
12 Ⓐ Ⓑ Ⓒ Ⓓ (B)	6, p. 136	Simple past: Irregular verbs
13 Ⓐ Ⓑ Ⓒ Ⓓ (A)	3, p. 130	Prepositions of time
14 Ⓐ Ⓑ Ⓒ Ⓓ (B)	9, p. 142	Ways to express reasons
15 Ⓐ Ⓑ Ⓒ Ⓓ (C)	9, p. 142	Ways to express reasons
16 Ⓐ Ⓑ Ⓒ Ⓓ (A)	6, p. 136	Simple past: Irregular verbs
17 Ⓐ Ⓑ Ⓒ Ⓓ (C)	3, p. 130	Prepositions of time
18 Ⓐ Ⓑ Ⓒ Ⓓ (A)	9, p. 142	Ways to express reasons
19 Ⓐ Ⓑ Ⓒ Ⓓ (C)	6, p. 136	Simple past: Irregular verbs
20 Ⓐ Ⓑ Ⓒ Ⓓ (B)	3, p. 130	Ways to express reasons
21 Ⓐ Ⓑ Ⓒ Ⓓ (C)	9, p. 142	Ways to express reasons
22 Ⓐ Ⓑ Ⓒ Ⓓ (A)	1, p. 126	Identify health problems
23 Ⓐ Ⓑ Ⓒ Ⓓ (D)	1, p. 126	Identify health problems
24 Ⓐ Ⓑ Ⓒ Ⓓ (B)	1, p. 126	Identify health problems
25 Ⓐ Ⓑ Ⓒ Ⓓ (C)	1, p. 126	Identify health problems
26 Ⓐ Ⓑ Ⓒ Ⓓ (B)	4, p. 132	Read medicine labels
27 Ⓐ Ⓑ Ⓒ Ⓓ (D)	4, p. 132	Read medicine labels
28 Ⓐ Ⓑ Ⓒ Ⓓ (A)	4, p. 132	Read medicine labels
29 Ⓐ Ⓑ Ⓒ Ⓓ (B)	4, p. 132	Read medicine labels
30 Ⓐ Ⓑ Ⓒ Ⓓ (C)	4, p. 132	Read medicine labels
31 Ⓐ Ⓑ Ⓒ Ⓓ (B)	4, p. 132	Read medicine labels
32 Ⓐ Ⓑ Ⓒ Ⓓ (B)		Read for details
33 Ⓐ Ⓑ Ⓒ Ⓓ (B)		Read for details

Please see reverse for test audio script.

Unit 7 Test Audio Script

Listening I
(Track 25) Page 57. Look at the pictures and listen.
What is the correct answer: A, B, or C?

1. Terry is dizzy.
2. Fernando hurt his head.

Listening II
(Track 26) Page 58. Listen to the question and three answers.
What is the correct answer: A, B, or C?

3. Can you come on Wednesday at 2:00?
   A. What's the matter?
   B. My throat is swollen.
   C. Yes, that's fine.

4. What's the matter?
   A. I'm nauseous.
   B. I have an appointment at 2:30.
   C. I'm sorry to hear that.

(Track 27) Page 58. Listen to the conversation. Then listen to the question and three answers.
What is the correct answer: A, B, or C?

5. **M:** I can't come in today because my daughter has an earache.
   F: Sorry to hear that.

   What's the matter?
   A. The man is sick.
   B. The woman has an earache.
   C. The man's daughter has an earache.

6. **F:** I hurt my wrist in a soccer game. I think I sprained it.
   M: That's too bad.

   What happened to the woman?
   A. She burned her hand.
   B. She sprained her wrist.
   C. She fell and broke her arm.

Unit 8 Test Answer Key

ANSWERS	LESSON/PAGE	OBJECTIVE
1 (A) B C D	2, p. 148	Talk about skills at a job interview
2 A (B) C D	5, p. 154	Answer questions about work history
3 (A) B C D	8, p. 160	Answer questions about availability
4 A B (C) D	2, p. 148	Talk about skills at a job interview
5 A (B) C D	2, p. 148	Talk about skills at a job interview
6 A B (C) D	5, p. 154	Answer questions about work history
7 A B (C) D	3, p. 150	*Can* to express ability
8 (A) B C D	9, p. 162	Ways to express alternatives: *Or, and*
9 A B (C) D	6, p. 156	Time expressions with *ago, last, in,* and *later*
10 A B (C) D	3, p. 150	*Can* to express ability
11 A B (C) D	6, p. 156	Time expressions with *ago, last, in,* and *later*
12 A (B) C D	6, p. 156	Time expressions with *ago, last, in,* and *later*
13 A (B) C D	9, p. 162	Ways to express alternatives: *Or, and*
14 (A) B C D	3, p. 150	*Can* to express ability
15 A (B) C D	9, p. 162	Ways to express alternatives: *Or, and*
16 A B (C) D	3, p. 150	*Can* to express ability
17 (A) B C D	9, p. 162	Ways to express alternatives: *Or, and*
18 (A) B C D	6, p. 156	Time expressions with *ago, last, in,* and *later*
19 A (B) C D	3, p. 150	*Can* to express ability
20 A B (C) D	6, p. 156	Time expressions with *ago, last, in,* and *later*
21 (A) B C D	9, p. 162	Ways to express alternatives: *Or, and*
22 A B C (D)	1, p. 146	Identify job duties
23 A B (C) D	1, p. 146	Identify job duties
24 A B C (D)	1, p. 146	Identify job duties
25 (A) B C D	1, p. 146	Identify job duties
26 A (B) C D	4, p. 152	Read help-wanted ads
27 A B (C) D	4, p. 152	Read help-wanted ads
28 A B (C) D	4, p. 152	Read help-wanted ads
29 (A) B C D	LSW, p. 263	Complete a job application
30 A (B) C D	LSW, p. 263	Complete a job application
31 A B C (D)	LSW, p. 263	Complete a job application
32 A (B) C D		Read for details
33 A B (C) D		Read for details

Please see reverse for test audio script.

Unit 8 Test Audio Script

Listening I
(Track 28) Page 66. Look at the pictures and listen.
What is the correct answer: A, B, or C?

1. Can Teresa use a cash register?
2. Last year, Drew got a job as a warehouse worker.

Listening II
(Track 29) Page 67. Listen to the question and three answers.
What is the correct answer: A, B, or C?

3. Do you prefer to work mornings or afternoons?
   A. I prefer afternoons, but I am flexible.
   B. I came to the U.S. five years ago.
   C. In three weeks.

4. Can you speak Spanish?
   A. Things in my life have changed, and I'd like to do something different.
   B. I receive shipments and unload materials.
   C. No, I can't, but I can learn.

(Track 30) Page 67. Listen to the conversation. Then listen to the question and three answers.
What is the correct answer: A, B, or C?

5. **M:** What are your job duties?
   F: I prepare food and clean equipment.

   What does the woman do at work?
   A. She greets visitors.
   B. She prepares food and cleans equipment.
   C. She prepares food, but she doesn't clean equipment.

6. **F:** Why are you looking for another job?
   M: I'd like a job closer to home.

   What does the man want?
   A. to stay at his job
   B. to work on a different schedule
   C. to find a job closer to his house

Unit 9 Test Answer Key

	ANSWERS	LESSON/PAGE	OBJECTIVE
1	Ⓐ Ⓑ **C** Ⓓ	5, p. 174	Talk about progress in school
2	Ⓐ Ⓑ **C** Ⓓ	8, p. 180	Discuss a child's behavior in school
3	**A** Ⓑ Ⓒ Ⓓ	2, p. 168	Make plans for school events
4	Ⓐ Ⓑ **C** Ⓓ	5, p. 174	Talk about progress in school
5	Ⓐ Ⓑ **C** Ⓓ	8, p. 180	Discuss a child's behavior in school
6	Ⓐ **B** Ⓒ Ⓓ	5, p. 174	Talk about progress in school
7	**A** Ⓑ Ⓒ Ⓓ	4, p. 172	Take a phone message
8	Ⓐ Ⓑ **C** Ⓓ	4, p. 172	Take a phone message
9	Ⓐ **B** Ⓒ Ⓓ	6, p. 176	Adverbs of manner
10	Ⓐ Ⓑ **C** Ⓓ	3, p. 170	Future with *will*
11	Ⓐ Ⓑ **C** Ⓓ	6, p. 176	Adverbs of manner
12	Ⓐ Ⓑ **C** Ⓓ	9, p. 177	Object pronouns
13	Ⓐ Ⓑ **C** Ⓓ	9, p. 182	Possessive nouns
14	Ⓐ **B** Ⓒ Ⓓ	3, p. 170	Future with *will*
15	Ⓐ Ⓑ **C** Ⓓ	6, p. 176	Adverbs of manner
16	Ⓐ **B** Ⓒ Ⓓ	9, p. 182	Possessive nouns
17	**A** Ⓑ Ⓒ Ⓓ	9, p. 177	Object pronouns
18	Ⓐ **B** Ⓒ Ⓓ	3, p. 170	Future with *will*
19	**A** Ⓑ Ⓒ Ⓓ	9, p. 182	Possessive nouns
20	Ⓐ **B** Ⓒ Ⓓ	3, p. 170	Future with *will*
21	**A** Ⓑ Ⓒ Ⓓ	9, p. 177	Object pronouns
22	Ⓐ Ⓑ **C** Ⓓ	6, p. 176	Adverbs of manner
23	**A** Ⓑ Ⓒ Ⓓ	9, p. 177	Object pronouns
24	**A** Ⓑ Ⓒ Ⓓ	1, p. 166	Identify school subjects
25	Ⓐ Ⓑ Ⓒ **D**	1, p. 166	Identify school subjects
26	Ⓐ Ⓑ **C** Ⓓ	1, p. 166	Identify school subjects
27	Ⓐ **B** Ⓒ Ⓓ	1, p. 166	Identify school subjects
28	Ⓐ Ⓑ Ⓒ **D**	4, p. 172	Take a phone message
29	**A** Ⓑ Ⓒ Ⓓ	4, p. 172	Take a phone message
30	**A** Ⓑ Ⓒ Ⓓ	LSW, p. 264	Complete a school enrollment form
31	Ⓐ Ⓑ **C** Ⓓ	LSW, p. 264	Complete a school enrollment form
32	Ⓐ Ⓑ **C** Ⓓ		Read for details
33	Ⓐ **B** Ⓒ Ⓓ		Read for details

Please see reverse for test audio script.

Unit 9 Test Audio Script

Listening I
(Track 31) Page 75. Look at the pictures and listen.
What is the correct answer: A, B, or C?

1. Lee is having a little trouble in science class.
2. Maya is disrespectful to the teacher.

Listening II
(Track 32) Page 76. Listen to the question and three answers.
What is the correct answer: A, B, or C?

3. There's a parent-teacher conference next week.
   A. Oh, yeah? What day?
   B. That way we can both go.
   C. Let's all talk tonight after dinner.

4. John needs to study a little more.
   A. That's good to hear.
   B. I'll talk to him tonight.
   C. So, how's John doing?

(Track 33) Page 76. Listen to the conversation. Then listen to the question and three answers.
What is the correct answer: A, B, or C?

5. **M:** Leila's teacher said she's getting to school late and fooling around in class.
   F: We need to find out what's going on right away.

   How is Leila doing in school?
   A. She's getting to school on time.
   B. She's paying attention in class.
   C. She's fooling around in class.

6. **M:** Manuel does well in language arts. He writes well.
   F: That's good to hear. He studies hard.

   How is Manuel doing in school?
   A. He needs to study more.
   B. He writes well.
   C. He has trouble with language arts.

Life Skills I
(Track 34) Page 77. Look at the pictures and listen.
What is the correct answer: A, B, or C?

7. **M:** Ms. Mare isn't here right now. May I take a message?
   F: Yes, please. This is Lindsay Bolla. Please ask her to call me back at (917) 555-5454.

8. **M:** This is Parker Sanchez. Please ask Mr. Fong to call me about the parent-teacher conference. My number is (917) 333-5555.
   F: OK. I'll give Mr. Fong the message.

Unit 10 Test Answer Key

	ANSWERS	LESSON/PAGE	OBJECTIVE
1	Ⓐ Ⓑ **Ⓒ** Ⓓ	2, p. 188	Ask for quantities of food
2	Ⓐ Ⓑ **Ⓒ** Ⓓ	2, p. 188	Ask for quantities of food
3	Ⓐ **Ⓑ** Ⓒ Ⓓ	2, p. 188	Ask for quantities of food
4	Ⓐ Ⓑ **Ⓒ** Ⓓ	8, p. 200	Order food in a restaurant
5	Ⓐ Ⓑ **Ⓒ** Ⓓ	5, p. 194	Compare information in food ads
6	Ⓐ **Ⓑ** Ⓒ Ⓓ	8, p. 200	Order food in a restaurant
7	Ⓐ Ⓑ **Ⓒ** Ⓓ	3, p. 190	Count nouns/Non-count nouns
8	**Ⓐ** Ⓑ Ⓒ Ⓓ	6, p. 196	Comparative adjectives with *than*
9	**Ⓐ** Ⓑ Ⓒ Ⓓ	9, p. 202	Quantifiers with non-count nouns
10	**Ⓐ** Ⓑ Ⓒ Ⓓ	6, p. 196	Comparative adjectives with *than*
11	Ⓐ **Ⓑ** Ⓒ Ⓓ	3, p. 191	*How much/How many*
12	Ⓐ **Ⓑ** Ⓒ Ⓓ	9, p. 202	Quantifiers with plural nouns
13	**Ⓐ** Ⓑ Ⓒ Ⓓ	3, p. 190	Count nouns/Non-count nouns
14	Ⓐ **Ⓑ** Ⓒ Ⓓ	3, p. 191	*How much/How many*
15	Ⓐ Ⓑ **Ⓒ** Ⓓ	3, p. 190	Count nouns/Non-count nouns
16	Ⓐ Ⓑ **Ⓒ** Ⓓ	3, p. 190	Count nouns/Non-count nouns
17	Ⓐ **Ⓑ** Ⓒ Ⓓ	6, p. 196	Comparative adjectives with *than*
18	Ⓐ Ⓑ **Ⓒ** Ⓓ	9, p. 202	Quantifiers with plural nouns
19	**Ⓐ** Ⓑ Ⓒ Ⓓ	9, p. 202	Quantifiers with non-count nouns
20	Ⓐ **Ⓑ** Ⓒ Ⓓ	9, p. 202	Quantifiers with plural nouns
21	**Ⓐ** Ⓑ Ⓒ Ⓓ	6, p. 196	Comparative adjectives with *than*
22	Ⓐ **Ⓑ** Ⓒ Ⓓ	1, p. 186	Identify food containers and quantities
23	Ⓐ Ⓑ Ⓒ **Ⓓ**	1, p. 186	Identify food containers and quantities
24	Ⓐ Ⓑ **Ⓒ** Ⓓ	1, p. 186	Identify food containers and quantities
25	**Ⓐ** Ⓑ Ⓒ Ⓓ	1, p. 186	Identify food containers and quantities
26	Ⓐ Ⓑ Ⓒ **Ⓓ**	4, p. 193	Read nutrition information
27	Ⓐ **Ⓑ** Ⓒ Ⓓ	4, p. 193	Read nutrition information
28	**Ⓐ** Ⓑ Ⓒ Ⓓ	4, p. 193	Read nutrition information
29	Ⓐ Ⓑ **Ⓒ** Ⓓ	4, p. 193	Read nutrition information
30	Ⓐ Ⓑ **Ⓒ** Ⓓ	4, p. 192	Read nutrition information
31	**Ⓐ** Ⓑ Ⓒ Ⓓ	4, p. 192	Read nutrition information
32	Ⓐ Ⓑ **Ⓒ** Ⓓ		Read for details
33	Ⓐ **Ⓑ** Ⓒ Ⓓ		Read for details

Please see reverse for test audio script.

Unit 10 Test Audio Script

Listening I
(Track 35) Page 85. Look at the pictures and listen.
What is the correct answer: A, B, or C?

1. Could you get me a half-gallon of chocolate milk, please?
2. How many cans of baked beans?

Listening II
(Track 36) Page 86. Listen to the question and three answers.
What is the correct answer: A, B, or C?

3. Do you need anything from the store?
   A. I'll be back in a little while.
   B. Yes. I need some coffee.
   C. Sure, no problem.

4. And what would you like with that?
   A. Here you go.
   B. Could you get a gallon of apple cider?
   C. A side of French fries.

(Track 37) Page 86. Listen to the conversation. Then listen to the question and three answers.
What is the correct answer: A, B, or C?

5. **M:** What brand of orange juice do you buy, Shelley?
   F: I buy fresh orange juice. It's better for you.

   Why does Shelley buy fresh orange juice?
   A. It is easier to prepare.
   B. It tastes good.
   C. It's better for you.

6. **M:** Are you ready to order?
   F: Yes. I'd like the fish sandwich and a side of coleslaw.

   What does the woman want?
   A. roast chicken and a side of coleslaw
   B. a fish sandwich and a side of coleslaw
   C. a fish sandwich and a side of mashed potatoes

Unit 11 Test Answer Key

	ANSWERS	LESSON/PAGE	OBJECTIVE
1	(A) B C D	2, p. 208	Call 911 to report a medical emergency
2	A (B) C D	8, p. 220	Respond to a police officer's instructions
3	A (B) C D	8, p. 220	Respond to a police officer's instructions
4	A B (C) D	2, p. 208	Call 911 to report a medical emergency
5	A (B) C D	5, p. 214	Describe an emergency
6	A B (C) D	2, p. 208	Call 911 to report a medical emergency
7	A (B) C D	3, p. 210	Present continuous: Statements and questions
8	(A) B C D	9, p. 222	Compound imperatives
9	(A) B C D	3, p. 210	Present continuous: Statements and questions
10	A B (C) D	6, p. 216	*There was/There were*
11	(A) B C D	9, p. 222	Compound imperatives
12	A B (C) D	3, p. 210	Present continuous: Statements and questions
13	A (B) C D	3, p. 210	Present continuous: Statements and questions
14	(A) B C D	6, p. 216	*There was/There were*
15	(A) B C D	9, p. 222	Compound imperatives
16	A (B) C D	9, p. 222	Compound imperatives
17	A B (C) D	6, p. 216	*There was/There were*
18	(A) B C D	9, p. 222	Compound imperatives
19	A (B) C D	6, p. 216	*There was/There were*
20	A B (C) D	3, p. 210	Present continuous: Statements and questions
21	A (B) C D	3, p. 210	Present continuous: Statements and questions
22	A (B) C D	1, p. 206	Identify medical emergencies
23	(A) B C D	1, p. 206	Identify medical emergencies
24	A B (C) D	1, p. 206	Identify medical emergencies
25	A B C (D)	1, p. 206	Identify medical emergencies
26	(A) B C D	4, p. 212	Understand fire safety procedures
27	(A) B C D	4, p. 212	Understand fire safety procedures
28	(A) B C D	4, p. 212	Understand fire safety procedures
29	A B C (D)	4, p. 212	Understand fire safety procedures
30	A (B) C D	4, p. 212	Understand fire safety procedures
31	A (B) C D		Read for details
32	A B C (D)		Read for details
33	A B (C) D		Read for details

Please see reverse for test audio script.

Unit 11 Test Audio Script

Listening I
(Track 38) Page 94. Look at the pictures and listen.
What is the correct answer: A, B, or C?

1. I think my child swallowed poison!
2. He pulled me over for tailgating.

Listening II
(Track 39) Page 95. Listen to the question and three answers.
What is the correct answer: A, B, or C?

3. I need to see your license, proof of insurance, and registration.
   A. I'm not sure.
   B. OK. They're in my glove compartment.
   C. You can get them.

4. What's the location of the emergency?
   A. A man is unconscious.
   B. This is Angelica Torres.
   C. Melvin's Deli at 420 Main Street.

(Track 40) Page 95. Listen to the conversation. Then listen to the question and three answers.
What is the correct answer: A, B, or C?

5. **M:** What happened last night?
   F: There was a car accident. Three people were hurt.

   What happened?
   A. No one was hurt.
   B. There was a car accident.
   C. There was a construction accident.

6. **F:** 9-1-1. What's your emergency?
   M: I think a woman burned herself.

   What is happening?
   A. A woman is unconscious.
   B. A woman fell.
   C. A woman burned herself.

Unit 12 Test Answer Key

ANSWERS	LESSON/PAGE	OBJECTIVE
1 (A) (B) **(C)** (D)	2, p. 228	Ask about policies at work
2 (A) **(B)** (C) (D)	5, p. 234	Ask a co-worker to cover your hours
3 (A) (B) **(C)** (D)	2, p. 228	Ask about policies at work
4 **(A)** (B) (C) (D)	5, p. 234	Ask a co-worker to cover your hours
5 **(A)** (B) (C) (D)	5, p. 234	Ask a co-worker to cover your hours
6 (A) (B) **(C)** (D)	8, p. 240	Request a schedule change
7 (A) **(B)** (C) (D)	3, p. 230	Expressions of necessity: *must/have to*
8 (A) (B) **(C)** (D)	6, p. 237	Information questions with *what/which/what/where*
9 (A) (B) **(C)** (D)	3, p. 230	Expressions of prohibition: *must not/can't*
10 (A) **(B)** (C) (D)	9, p. 242	*Can/Could* to ask permission
11 **(A)** (B) (C) (D)	6, p. 236	Information questions with *who*
12 (A) (B) **(C)** (D)	6, p. 236	Information questions with *who*
13 (A) (B) **(C)** (D)	3, p. 230	Expressions of necessity: *must/have to*
14 (A) **(B)** (C) (D)	9, p. 242	*Can/Could* to ask permission
15 (A) **(B)** (C) (D)	6, p. 237	Information questions with *what/which/what/where*
16 (A) **(B)** (C) (D)	3, p. 230	Expressions of necessity: *must/have to*
17 **(A)** (B) (C) (D)	9, p. 242	*Can/Could* to ask permission
18 (A) (B) **(C)** (D)	6, p. 236	Information questions with *who*
19 (A) (B) **(C)** (D)	9, p. 242	*Can/Could* to ask permission
20 (A) **(B)** (C) (D)	3, p. 230	Expressions of prohibition: *must not/can't*
21 (A) (B) **(C)** (D)	9, p. 242	*Can/Could* to ask permission
22 **(A)** (B) (C) (D)	1, p. 226	Identify job responsibilities
23 (A) (B) (C) **(D)**	1, p. 226	Identify job responsibilities
24 (A) **(B)** (C) (D)	1, p. 226	Identify job responsibilities
25 (A) (B) **(C)** (D)	1, p. 226	Identify job responsibilities
26 **(A)** (B) (C) (D)	4, p. 232	Read a pay stub
27 (A) (B) **(C)** (D)	4, p. 232	Read a pay stub
28 (A) (B) **(C)** (D)	4, p. 232	Read a pay stub
29 (A) (B) **(C)** (D)	4, p. 232	Read a pay stub
30 **(A)** (B) (C) (D)	LSW, p. 267	Complete a vacation request form
31 (A) (B) **(C)** (D)	LSW, p. 267	Complete a vacation request form
32 **(A)** (B) (C) (D)		Read for details
33 **(A)** (B) (C) (D)		Read for details

Please see reverse for test audio script.

Unit 12 Test Audio Script

Listening I
(Track 41) Page 103. Look at the pictures and listen.
What is the correct answer: A, B, or C?

1. You have to wear a uniform at work.
2. I can't come in. I have to go to the dentist.

Listening II
(Track 42) Page 104. Listen to the question and three answers.
What is the correct answer: A, B, or C?

3. Am I allowed to eat at my desk?
   A. I'm glad I asked.
   B. What do you want to know?
   C. No, you aren't.

4. Can I ask you a favor, Louise?
   A. Sure. What is it?
   B. I'm on the schedule for Tuesday.
   C. I'll get back to you.

(Track 43) Page 104. Listen to the conversation. Then listen to the question and three answers.
What is the correct answer: A, B, or C?

5. **M:** I have to go to the doctor on Friday. Can you take my shift for me?
   F: No problem.

   What is the woman going to do on Friday?
   A. go to the doctor
   B. take the man's shift for him
   C. take the day off

6. **F:** My hours changed at my other job. Could I change to mornings?
   M: Well, let me look at the schedule.

   What does the woman want to do?
   A. She wants to get another job.
   B. She wants to work in the evenings.
   C. She wants to work in the mornings.